The Personal Development Guide

The COA guide to exploring gap year activities, improving your grades and getting a taste of higher education

Edited by
Ken Reynolds

The Personal Development Guide

This 8th edition published in 2014 by Cambridge Occupational Analysts Ltd
Sparham, Norwich, NR9 5PR

Editorial and Publishing Team

Editor Ken Reynolds
Cover Design PFD
Design and typesetting Simon Foster and Paul Rankin
Illustrations Diana Mainstone

© Cambridge Occupational Analysts Ltd 2014

British Library Cataloguing in Publication Data
A catalogue record for this book is available from the British Library.

ISBN 978-1-906711-21-4

Typeset by Cambridge Occupational Analysts Ltd, Sparham, Norwich NR9 5PR
Printed and bound in Great Britain by Clays Ltd, Bungay, Suffolk NR35 1ED

Disclaimer

While every effort has been made to ensure that all information in this book is up-to-date and accurate, and that all organisations listed are bona fide providers of opportunities for young people to develop their personal, learning and thinking skills, inclusion should not necessarily be assumed to be a recommendation. The authors do not accept any liability for errors, omissions or apparently misleading statements, nor for any loss, illness, injury or inconvenience resulting from the use of the information supplied. Readers must research all options with extreme thoroughness and reach their own judgment regarding the most suitable.

Contents

Introduction

This book is about exploring ideas that could help you in your future personal and career development. It is aimed primarily at young people aged around 16 to 18. We envisage that most readers will be working towards AS/A levels, IB, Highers or equivalent and will be in the sixth form/Year 12 or Scottish Year 5 (Y12/S5) at school or college. You may be starting to research possible courses in higher education, perhaps contemplating a Gap Year before going to university, and wondering what on earth you'll be able to write in your application that will have admissions tutors queuing up to recruit such an admirable student!

Our goal is to present you with a series of suggestions and exercises that will give you an idea of the many opportunities available and an understanding of how best to match these opportunities to your own needs.

In the first section of the book, we offer our own broad classification of the astonishing range of courses, projects, trips and treks that you could use to nurture your own set of personal, learning and thinking skills.

Our nine headings are:

1. International Community Projects

2. Non-specific Organisations

3. Study, Sports-related and Cultural Options

4. Treks/Expeditions and Activity Holidays

5. Industry/Employment

6. Nature/Conservation

7. Community Projects in the UK

8. Teaching

9. Specific Country-based Organisations

Should you wish to improve your grades by re-taking examinations or by seeking extra tuition for your current studies, the second section of our book lists colleges offering this type of provision. Finally, we give details of Taster courses, provided by many universities and colleges to allow you to experience something of the academic and social life of an undergraduate student before you make a formal application for a place in higher education.

Developing essential skills

Whatever you decide to do, try to look beyond the admittedly important elements of fun and excitement to think about whether your chosen activities will help develop the skills regarded as essential for success in education, training, work and life in general.

These skills involve written and spoken communication, using numbers and using computers. They are relevant for everyone, from the youngest pupils in school to the most senior executives in global organisations. With the help of this book, not to mention time spent analysing your needs and exploring appropriate options, you should be able to improve the quality of your learning and performance by acquiring the ability to apply essential skills in different contexts.

The sheer number of agencies offering opportunities for young people can be bewildering, so we have grouped them under our own headings to help you become aware of the range of possibilities and decide what sort of activity best meets your needs. Please note, however, that many organisations offer such a variety of opportunities that they could easily be placed under several headings.

You can spend your time in the UK or overseas; you may be paid or you may have to pay a considerable sum in order to participate; you may choose a course of study or you may go on an expedition. Or maybe you have simply been stuck in the classroom for too long and need to get out in the fresh air and discover the delights of the great outdoors. This could feature environmental conservation work, sports coaching or some madcap white-knuckle adventure. The choice is yours.

Also in this series:

    The Careers Directory

    60 Successful Personal Statements for UCAS Application

    Degree Course Descriptions

    All titles published by COA Ltd **www.coa.co.uk**

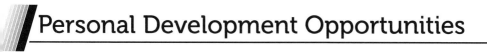

Personal Development Opportunities

1. International Community Projects

The aim of these projects is usually to offer humanitarian aid to communities living in poverty, to provide healthcare for the chronically sick, to rebuild homes destroyed by floods and so on. Some schemes ask for volunteers with skills in, say, construction or healthcare. You may have to pay – sometimes several thousand pounds – to participate.

You should be aware that some projects of this type are derided by critics as mere 'voluntourism', taking jobs away from local people who really need them in order to help wealthy westerners feel good about themselves. There are even suggestions that the problem of fake orphanages in Cambodia, for example, is seriously damaging family life. It is claimed that children are being unnecessarily separated from their families just to take advantage of the resources lavished upon them by well-intentioned but misguided volunteers. According to the pressure group Orphanages No (visit their website at: **www.orphanages.no**), some three quarters of children living in Cambodian orphanages are not orphans at all but simply come from poor families. It is essential that you research providers and projects carefully to be sure that you and your money will bring positive benefit to a community...and, perhaps more importantly, will not be doing any harm.

A reputable organisation should be able to tell you how the fees it charges are being spent, to show you its responsible tourism policy, and to put you in touch both with participants from previous years and with locals on the ground. Look, for example, at reviews on social media, such as Facebook's Better Volunteering community at: **http://facebook.com/BetterVolunteering**

In short, ask the right questions before you make any commitment and plan carefully. Then you can be confident that your skills will be put to good use.

Agape Volunteers   17+

Agape Volunteers provide opportunities in a wide range of well-established, affordable volunteer placements to support humanitarian work in Kenya, Maasai-land, Ghana, South Africa and Tanzania. They organise opportunities to teach in a school, work in an orphanage, develop sports education programmes and work in conservation. Medical students can join one of the hands-on placements in an African hospital or clinic. Placements are geared towards making a difference and volunteers are guaranteed hard work and a life-changing trip.

Countries: Ghana, Kenya, Maasai-land, South Africa, Tanzania

Twitter: @AgapeVolunteer

Web: **www.agape-volunteers.com**

Big Beyond   18+

Big Beyond organises ethical volunteer placements in Africa for adventurous individuals looking for experiences far beyond the norm, off the beaten path and with the chance to become immersed in another culture. Volunteer placements are always tailored to your skills, interests and level of experience, as well as the needs of the local community. There are currently project sites in Uganda, Malawi and Ethiopia. Volunteer involvement ranges from education, enterprise and environment to health- or culture-related projects.

Countries: Uganda, Malawi, Ethiopia

Twitter: @BigBeyond

Web: **www.bigbeyond.org**

Experiment in International Living   16+

Your community service as an EIL Volunteer for International Partnership (VIP) could be working with a rural development project, volunteering in a health clinic, working with children or teaching English. VIP offers individuals or groups the opportunity to volunteer abroad in over 20 countries. Most programmes include language training and homestays with families – an excellent way to meet people and learn about local culture.

Countries: Albania, Argentina, Brazil, Canada, Chile, China, Ecuador, Eire, France, Germany, Guatemala, Ghana, Italy, Japan, Korea, Malta, Mexico, Morocco, New Zealand, Nigeria, South Africa, Spain, Turkey, UK,

Web: **www.eiluk.org**

Global Volunteer Network   15-17, 18+

This network offers volunteer opportunities in community projects throughout the world, currently providing volunteer programmes through partner organisations across South America, Asia and Africa. It also offers fundraising treks, and volunteer trips for 15- to 17-year-olds. The vision is to connect people with communities in need, with a particular focus on vulnerable women and children. This is done by supporting the work of local community organisations in countries through the placement of international volunteers.

Countries: Argentina, Brazil, Costa Rica, Ecuador, Ethiopia, Fiji, Kenya, Nepal, New Zealand, Panama, Peru, Philippines, Rwanda, Seychelles, South Africa, USA, Thailand, Uganda, Vietnam

Twitter: @GVNnFoundation

Web: **www.globalvolunteernetwork.org**

Global Volunteer Projects   17+

This organisation offers a variety of placements and projects across the world including medical placements, teaching projects, HIV awareness projects, journalism placements, conservation projects and orphanage placements. You could find yourself working at a Ghanaian TV station, at an orphanage in Cambodia or helping to preserve endangered sea turtles on the Pacific coast of Mexico.

Countries: Cambodia, China, Ghana, India, Mexico, Romania, Tanzania

Web: **www.globalvolunteerprojects.org**

GVI Foundations   15-17

Global Vision International (GVI) has sent over 10,000 volunteers overseas to aid critical environmental and humanitarian programmes, working hand in hand with local communities, international and local charities and governmental organisations to ensure long-term sustainability. GVI has created specially designed projects for young adults, a blend of volunteering, cultural and adventure activities.

Countries: Costa Rica, Fiji, Greece, Kenya, India, Peru, South Africa, Thailand

Twitter: @GVIFoundations

Web: **www.gvi.co.uk/volunteer-options/under-18**

Habitat for Humanity   16+

An international aid charity working to end poverty housing around the world, Habitat for Humanity works in over 3,000 communities in 70 countries. Volunteer teams work alongside local communities and housing beneficiaries to provide them with a safe and decent place to live.

Countries: 70+ countries around the world

Twitter: @HabitatFHGB

Web: **www.habitatforhumanity.org.uk**

i-to-i Volunteering   17+

For the last 20 years i-to-i has been sending volunteers to contribute within underprivileged communities in Africa, Asia, Australasia and Latin America. 50,000 volunteers have made a difference abroad with i-to-i. All i-to-i projects overseas are based in the local community and are local initiatives. When you travel with i-to-i, you will stay in locally run accommodation and travel on locally owned transport.

Countries: Australia, Belize, Brazil, Cambodia, China, Costa Rica, Ecuador, Fiji, Ghana, Guatemala, India, Indonesia, Kenya, Malawi, Malaysia, Mozambique, Namibia, Nepal, New Zealand, Peru, South Africa, Sri Lanka, Swaziland, Tanzania, Thailand, Uganda, Vietnam, Zambia

Twitter: @itoiranger

Web: **www.i-to-i.com**

International Voluntary Service (IVS GB)   18+

A peace organisation working for the sustainable development of local and global communities throughout the world, IVS GB is the British branch of Service Civil International, a worldwide network of like-minded voluntary organisations promoting peace and justice through voluntary work. By taking part in an international voluntary project, you will be working and living alongside other volunteers from all over the world and contributing to local community development. There are hundreds of projects to choose from, including environmental conservation on beaches in Morocco, help at a centre for children with disabilities in Latvia, work with elderly people in mountain villages in Japan, a community theatre in the Czech Republic, or youth work in Russia.

Countries: Worldwide

Twitter: @IVSGB

Web: **www.ivsgb.org**

Lattitude Global Volunteering   17-25

Lattitude organises voluntary work overseas, and similar exchange voluntary opportunities for overseas nationals in the UK. Lattitude volunteers work alongside staff in such roles as foreign language assistants, helping with general activities in schools, caring for the disadvantaged, or in outdoor education and conservation work. Whatever the nature of your placement, it will always be a challenge. You could be working in an environment different from anything you've ever experienced, so you need to adapt to your responsibilities with maturity. As well as making a real difference to the lives of others, you'll certainly learn a lot about yourself.

Countries: Argentina, Australia, Canada, China, Ecuador, Fiji, France, Ghana, India, Japan, Malawi, New Zealand, Poland, South Africa, Vanuatu, Vietnam

Twitter: @LattitudeUK

Web: **www.lattitude.org.uk**

Love Volunteers   15-17, 18+

Love Volunteers offers 'not-for-profit programme fees' for fun, rewarding, safe and affordable volunteering opportunities in developing countries around the world. Love Volunteers has a variety of programmes available, whether you're planning a week helping a local community as you travel around a country, want to spend six months learning the local language or are putting your gap year to good use.

Countries: Albania, Bangladesh, Cambodia, Cameroon, China, Costa Rica, Ecuador, Ethiopia, Ghana, Honduras, India, Kenya, Malawi, Mexico, Moldova, Mongolia, Morocco, Nepal, Palestine, Peru, Russia, Senegal, South Africa, Sri Lanka, Tanzania, Thailand, Uganda, Ukraine

Twitter: @LoveVolunteer

Web: **www.lovevolunteers.org**

Madventurer   17+

Madventurer rural projects focus on building basic infrastructure to assist local community development. The key focus is youth development and the provision and improvement of health and education through work on schools, clinics, toilets, water storage tanks, community centres and sanitation facilities. Venturers also have the opportunity to teach English and other subjects in local primary schools, as well as getting involved in extracurricular activities such as sports, art and drama. As a volunteer, you become part of the Mad Tribe. The spirit of volunteering brings together all shapes and sizes and accents. Each year there is a Mad World Ball in Newcastle upon Tyne, for reunions and reminiscing of the time you've weathered and treasured together.

Twitter: @Madventurer

Web: **www.madventurer.com**

Outreach International   16+

This specialist organisation has a wide variety of projects, all of them small, grassroots initiatives working with communities where volunteer work can make a big difference. Placements last between one month and twelve months and could involve anything from working with children – in schools or orphanages – to helping out at an animal rescue centre. Other projects include rainforest and marine conservation, teaching English or art and craft, or medical-related projects, such as community medicine and physiotherapy.

Countries: Cambodia, Costa Rica, Ecuador, Galápagos Islands, Kenya, Tanzania, Mexico, Nepal, Sri Lanka

Twitter: @Outreachint

Web: www.outreachinternational.co.uk

People and Places: responsible volunteering   18+

A winner at the 2013 World Responsible Tourism Awards, People and Places believes that "There are still way too many unethical or poorly managed volunteer organisations operating. We believe volunteering can be a win-win for volunteers and the community they seek to serve – but people must be put in the right places. So there needs to be a lot of information shared by all parties. If you can reserve a place on a volunteer programme simply by providing contact details and your credit card number, and if you don't know where exactly you'll be working and what you'll be doing, ask yourself: should I be volunteering with that organisation?"

Countries: Cambodia, Gambia, India, Kenya, Madagascar, Morocco, Nepal, Peru, Romania, Saint Lucia, South Africa, Swaziland, UK

Twitter: @BuildingBetterW

Web: http://travel-peopleandplaces.co.uk

PoD Volunteer   16+

PoD is a non-profit organisation arranging ethical and supported volunteering opportunities around the world. It works with long-term projects where there is genuine benefit to local communities. Whether it is for one week or six months, volunteers are needed to help work with disadvantaged children, communities, animals and conservation projects in Belize, Cambodia, Ghana, India, Nepal, Peru, South Africa, Thailand and Vietnam.

Countries: Belize, Cambodia, Ghana, India, Nepal, Peru, South Africa, Thailand, Vietnam

Twitter: @podvolunteer

Web: **www.podvolunteer.org**

Project Trust   17-19

Based on the Isle of Coll, Project Trust specialises in 12- or 8-month volunteer placements, giving you plenty of time to explore your new surroundings whilst working in the local community. You can choose from over 20 different countries, spending a year living, working and travelling in Africa, Asia, Latin America or the Caribbean with a wide variety of work and a diverse range of cultures.

Countries: Botswana, Cambodia, Chile, China, Dominican Republic, Ghana, Guyana, Honduras, Hong Kong, India, Japan, Malawi, Malaysia, Mauritius, Namibia, Nepal, Peru, Senegal, South Africa, Sri Lanka, Swaziland, Thailand

Twitter: @ProjectTrustUK

Web: **www.projecttrust.org.uk**

Restless Development   18-28

If you are passionate about changing lives and want to make a difference to the community that you work with, you can volunteer to work for five to eleven months in India, Zambia, Uganda, Tanzania, South Africa or Nepal. You might find yourself helping vulnerable young people protect themselves against HIV, open a library or a youth centre, construct a smokeless stove or establish a recycling programme.

Countries: India, Nepal, Sierra Leone, South Africa, Tanzania, Uganda, UK, USA, Zambia, Zimbabwe

Twitter: @RestlessDev

Web: **www.restlessdevelopment.org**

Travellers Worldwide   17+

Offering a variety of voluntary projects lasting from two weeks to a year, Travellers Worldwide seeks to help children, adults, animals and entire communities in less advantaged countries. The only qualifications you need are a spirit of adventure and a sense of humour.

Countries: Argentina, Australia, Brazil, Cambodia, China, Ecuador, Ghana, India, Malaysia, Mauritius, Morocco, Mozambique, Nepal, New Zealand, Peru, South Africa, Sri Lanka, Thailand, USA, Zambia, Zimbabwe

Twitter: @TravellersWW

Web: **www.travellersworldwide.com**

Volunteer Action for Peace 18+

Volunteer Action for Peace (VAP) is a UK-based charity organisation which works towards creating and preserving international peace, justice and human solidarity for people and their communities. Through a range of working projects both in the United Kingdom and around the world, VAP provides volunteers with opportunities to work together with people from around the globe and in partnership with local groups to enhance and empower communities. Opportunities vary from two to four weeks to six-plus months.

Countries: Worldwide

Twitter: @VAP_UK

Web: **www.vap.org.uk**

VSO ICS 18-25

VSO ICS is a once-in-a-lifetime programme that brings together 18 to 25-year-olds from all backgrounds to fight poverty overseas. Funded by the UK government, it offers volunteers the opportunity to contribute to genuine development projects by working for three months in Africa or Asia, alongside young in-country volunteers, whilst gaining transferable skills and experience. You don't need cash, skills or qualifications to volunteer with VSO ICS – just the ambition to make a difference.

Countries: Bangladesh, Cambodia, Ethiopia, India, Kenya, Nepal, Nigeria, Philippines, Sierra Leone, Tajikistan, Tanzania, Zambia, Zimbabwe

Twitter: @VSOUK

Web: **www.vso.org.uk/volunteer/opportunities/vso-ics-for-18-25-year-olds**

Worldwide Volunteering   16+

WWV believes in the power of voluntary work as a catalyst for change. It specialises in the use of volunteering to enable young people and people at risk of being marginalised to take control of their lives and expand their horizons, enhancing wellbeing, employability and life satisfaction.

Twitter: @WWV_Volunteer

Web: **www.wwv.org.uk**

2. Non-specific Organisations

Agencies listed here do not specialise in any one particular type of project. Some activities may be paid, some unpaid, while some are predominantly study-based. Typical offerings might include Volunteering (Community Development, Construction, Conservation, Teaching), Internships (Media, Marketing, Health, Tourism, Sports Coaching), Tours (Cultural, Ecological, Humanitarian, Train) and Jobs (all over the world). We have also listed under this heading some associations – such as the Year Out Group – acting as an umbrella group for several separate providers.

Africa and Asia Venture   18-25

AV, as it is generally known, recruits 18 to 25-year-olds, who want to combine four to five months of travel, safaris, adventure, friendship and fun in a year out with teaching or coaching sports, working with local communities or conservation work. You would normally start with a four-day in-country training course, then spend three to four months at your project, followed by one month of travel and safari. The latter could include seeing wildlife in African National Parks, visiting temples and palaces in Nepal, or adventure in Mexico. In Thailand, you would teach among the hill tribes for two months, followed by one month's project work, three weeks of travel/ adventure opportunities and a five-day open water diving course.

Countries: China, Ecuador, India, Kenya, Malawi, Mexico, Nepal, South Africa, Tanzania, Thailand, Uganda

Twitter: @AVentureUK

Web: **www.aventure.co.uk**

BUNAC   18+

BUNAC offers a wide range of working holidays in Australia, New Zealand, Canada and the USA, including the Summer Camp Exchange USA programme, and internships and volunteering programmes on marine, conservation, teaching and wildlife projects throughout the world from Fiji to South Africa. These are open to 18-year-olds and over in the UK, the USA and Ireland. Programmes last from 12 days up to two years.

Countries: Australia, Canada, Nepal, New Zealand, South Africa, USA, Cambodia, Thailand, Ecuador, China, Borneo, Costa Rica, Tanzania, Mexico and the Seychelles

Twitter: @BUNAC_UK

Web: **www.bunac.org/uk**

Changing Worlds   17+

Changing Worlds is a travel organisation that provides travel experiences for individuals looking to take part in placements overseas during a gap year, career break or as part of a constructive trip abroad. Placements range from career development, internships and work experience, courses and qualifications, paid work options and community volunteering to cultural and adventure tours.

Countries: Argentina, Australia, Cambodia, Canada, China, Ecuador, Germany, Ghana, India, Indonesia, Kenya, New Zealand, South Africa, Saint Lucia, Thailand, Vietnam

Twitter: @Changing_Worlds

Web: **www.changingworlds.co.uk**

Concordia   16-30

In addition to UK farm placements, Concordia offers an extensive international volunteer programme. Short-term projects bring together individuals from around the world to participate in two- to four-week projects in Western, Eastern and Central Europe, North America, North Africa, Japan and South Korea, or in Africa, Asia and Latin America. Medium-term projects usually last between one and six months, although they occasionally last for a whole year. Every Spring Concordia posts its new Summer programme for the forthcoming year.

Countries: Worldwide

Twitter: @ConcordiaVol

Web: **www.concordiavolunteers.org.uk**

Ecoteer   18+

Ecoteer works by providing a site where volunteers can find a variety of opportunities. By eliminating the middleman, the cost of volunteering is greatly reduced and more people have the chance to volunteer abroad. All volunteering enquiries go straight to the projects, so you can trust all the information you get is 100% accurate and up-to-date. Ecoteer covers opportunities at eco lodges, conservation, farm, teaching and humanitarian projects worldwide. It offers different types of placement such as ecotourism in Malaysia, sea turtle conservation in Costa Rica, or humanitarian and teaching projects in Ecuador.

Countries: Worldwide

Twitter: @ecoteer

Web: **www.ecoteer.com**

Edge of Africa   18+

Edge of Africa is an award-winning volunteer project co-ordinator for gap year placements, work experience and volunteer internships in Africa. Its conservation work includes lemur research, elephant and cheetah care and black rhino breeding, while there are also volunteer projects in the community and internships in such fields as criminology and marketing in South Africa.

Countries: Madagascar, South Africa, Zimbabwe

Twitter: @EDGEofAFRICA

Web: **www.edgeofafrica.com**

GapGuru   18+

GapGuru is a gap year specialist offering a wide range of volunteer, travel and internship opportunities across Asia, Africa, South America and Europe. With GapGuru you could be teaching English in Ecuador, working as a medical intern in India, building schools in Tanzania or even trekking up Mount Kilimanjaro! GapGuru gives you the opportunity to discover new countries and cultures, to meet new people and immerse yourself in local communities. Volunteers work in underprivileged communities, helping those in genuine need, while building their own skills, confidence and experience.

Countries: Thailand, Cambodia, Nepal, India, Tanzania, Romania, Peru

Twitter: @GapYearGuru

Web: **www.gapguru.com**

Gapwork   17+

The Gapwork website aims to provide everything you might need to know about taking a gap year and working abroad. It offers gap year and backpacking information, including news of gap year jobs, travel destinations and volunteering ideas, as well as a comprehensive planning section. Whether it's skiing in the Rocky Mountains, volunteering in a South African safari park or tracking river dolphins in the Amazon, there could be something suitable in the Gapwork activities section. Other sections include jobs, community development, sports and study abroad.

Twitter: @GapworkJobs

Web: **www.gapwork.com**

Global Choices   17+

Global Choices offers a wide variety of programmes for students, working with partner organisations all over the world to arrange job placements and volunteering opportunities. You could spend some time working in a hotel in Argentina, teaching English in Brazil or Spain, or you could travel to the US and earn a modest wage. You could try a working holiday programme in Australia or a summer in Camp USA. How about helping a disadvantaged community or taking part in a conservation programme? Global Choices has a vast range of programmes all over the world to help individuals enhance their professional and personal skills.

Countries: Worldwide

Twitter: @GlobalChoices

Web: **www.globalchoices.co.uk**

IST Plus   17+

With an IST Plus cultural exchange programme you can work, study, travel or teach in locations throughout the world. Work in the USA, teach in Thailand or China, travel around Australia and New Zealand and Singapore, or study a language anywhere in the world.

Countries: Australia, Cambodia, China, New Zealand, Singapore, Thailand, USA

Twitter: @ISTPlusWorld

Web: **www.istplus.com**

Overseas Job Centre   All ages

This site is a guide to living and working abroad, seasonal jobs, working holidays, careers breaks, gap years, volunteer work and long-term world travel. It lists volunteer work opportunities around the world, from tourism and catering to teaching or working with animals. It gives advice on planning your gap year as well as a useful list of websites for reference and further information.

Twitter: @WorkingTravellr

Web: **www.overseasjobcentre.co.uk**

Oyster Worldwide   18+

Oyster is an experienced gap and responsible travel organisation that has been sending volunteers and paid workers to diverse destinations since 1999. Volunteering projects include: childcare, teaching English, sports coaching, animal welfare and environmental conservation. Paid work opportunities include: ski instructing, hospitality work, farm work and teaching English. Oyster also offers medical, veterinary and business internship experiences.

Countries: Australia, Borneo, Brazil, Canada, Chile, China, Costa Rica, France, Namibia, Nepal, Romania, South Africa, Tanzania, Thailand

Twitter: @OysterWorldwide

Web: **www.oysterworldwide.com**

Pacific Discovery   18-24

Pacific Discovery offers inspiring gap year, experiential and educational travel programmes to the most amazing places on earth. Its award-winning programmes blend meaningful and challenging travel, cultural immersion, personal and leadership development, outdoors and wilderness exploration, volunteer and community service projects, ethical travel and sustainability focus.

Countries: Australia, Cambodia, Ecuador, Fiji, Galápagos Islands, Laos, Nepal, New Zealand, Peru, Thailand, Tibet, Vietnam

Twitter: @pacificdiscovry

Web: **www.pacificdiscovery.org**

Projects Abroad   16+

With a wide range of projects, including teaching, care, conservation, medicine and healthcare and journalism, Projects Abroad organises overseas voluntary work placements designed specifically for the communities where it works. The teaching projects focus on conversational English teaching and don't require TEFL qualifications. You could teach in Africa, Asia, Latin America or Eastern Europe, as part of a project in a school, university or orphanage. In journalism, you could work on a Chinese, Indian, Ghanaian, Mexican, Moldovan, Mongolian, Romanian or Sri Lankan newspaper or work at a radio station in Ghana, Senegal or Mexico, or even a TV station in Mongolia. A range of medical, conservation, animal care, business and sports internships are also available.

Countries: Worldwide

Twitter: @Proj_Abroad_UK

Web: **www.projects-abroad.co.uk**

Quest Overseas   17+

Specialists in Africa and South America, Quest offer 'Combined Gap Expeditions', in which you can learn a language, work on a community or conservation project and then explore the best of the surrounding countries. This could lead, for example, to Community Development work in Tanzania or a Game Reserve project in Swaziland, together with exploration of southern Africa, or an Animal Sanctuary project in Bolivia, together with exploration of the Andes.

Twitter: @QuestOverseas

Web: **www.questoverseas.com**

Real Gap Experience   17+

Real Gap Experience offers a comprehensive range of volunteering, paid work, sports, adventure travel, language courses and career breaks in over 40 countries, from two weeks to two years. The company can organise a complete gap year away unique to you (including flights and insurance) with a strong emphasis on security and safety. All Real Gap Experience advisers have taken their own gap year and will provide help and support to plan yours.

Countries: Worldwide

Twitter: @Real_Gap

Web: **www.realgap.co.uk**

Rotary Youth Exchange   15-19

Each year the Rotary Youth Exchange programme sends literally thousands of young people, on long- and short-term exchanges, special interest camps and tours. These aim to promote an insight into another country's way of life, traditions and culture, and to develop lasting friendships.

Web: **www.youthexchange.org.uk**

The Leap   17-27

The Leap offers adventurous volunteering team placements in Africa, South America and Asia, along with internship opportunities in Tanzania and Ecuador. Its projects aim to broaden your mind and your muscles and surpass your expectations.

Countries: Borneo, Cambodia, Costa Rica, Cuba, Ecuador, Kenya, Madagascar, South Africa, Tanzania, Venezuela

Twitter: @gapyearexperts

Web: **www.theleap.co.uk**

Twin Work and Volunteer   All ages

Twin Work and Volunteer provides a wide range of programmes allowing people of all backgrounds and ages the opportunity to participate in community and conservation volunteering projects around the world, together with internships and paid work placements. In a gap year abroad you could save endangered animals, build schools or work in an orphanage. You may want to volunteer for a community or conservation project or live and work abroad on a paid working holiday. Or you could add valuable work and life experience to your CV with an internship abroad or in the UK from four weeks to a year.

Countries: Worldwide

Twitter: @Work_Volunteer

Web: **www.workandvolunteer.com**

Year Out Group   17+

Formed in 1998 to promote the concept and benefits of well structured year out programmes, to promote models of good practice and to help young people and their advisers in selecting suitable and worthwhile projects, Year Out Group is a not-for-profit association of UK-registered organisations that specialise in this field. All the member organisations are carefully vetted on joining and provide annual confirmation that they continue to abide by the Group's Code of Practice and Operating Guidelines.

Countries: Worldwide

Twitter: @YearOutGroupOrg

Web: **www.yearoutgroup.org**

3. Study, Sports-related and Cultural Options

Organisations listed under this heading offer courses lasting anything from a day or two to around nine months. Courses may be academic, vocational or leisure-based. You will normally have to pay tuition fees, together with accommodation and travel costs. Options here include art and design, art history, business and IT skills, cookery, drama, fashion, journalism, languages, medicine, music, science, sport and veterinary studies.

ATOM (Advanced Topics on Medicine) Conference   15-18

This is a one-day conference designed to help Years 11, 12 and 13 students who want to hone their UCAS applications for Oxford, Cambridge and all other UK medical schools. It includes the following areas – impartial advice on UK medical schools, mock medical school interviews with feedback, before and after interview techniques, optional DVD of personal interviews and optional UCAS personal statement review.

Web: **www.atomconference.com**

Art History Abroad   16+

AHA's six-week course involves travelling throughout Italy to study at first hand many masterpieces of Italian art. The programme includes visits to Venice (10 nights), Verona (4 nights), Florence (10 nights), Siena (4 nights), Naples (4 nights) and Rome (10 nights), together with day excursions to at least six of: Padua, Vicenza, Ravenna, Modena, Urbino, Pisa, San Gimignano, Arezzo, Orvieto, Pompeii and Tivoli.

Twitter: @AHAcourses

Web: **www.arthistoryabroad.com**

Avenue Cookery School, London   16+

The Avenue Cookery School offers a variety of courses from basic to advanced, including 'The Really Useful Course', a five-day course for undergraduates and Gap Year students covering cooking and 'really useful' information. The relaxed and friendly atmosphere at The Avenue can turn even the most nervous beginner into a confident 'foodie'.

Twitter: @AvenueCookery

Web: **http://theavenuecookeryschool.com**

Ballymaloe Cookery School, Ireland   16+

Run by Ireland's most famous TV cook Darina Allen, Ballymaloe offers a highly regarded 12-week certificate course, graduates of which are in demand all over the world. There is also a wide range of shorter courses – some suitable for complete beginners, others aimed at more experienced cooks. A special time every day is lunch, when teachers and students sit down together to enjoy a three-course meal, which the students have prepared using recipes from the demonstrations. After school is over for the day, if the weather is good then there are plenty of outdoor activities – tennis, swimming, walking or just lounging around in the beautiful gardens.

Twitter: @Ballymaloe

Web: **www.cookingisfun.ie**

Brighton Journalist Works 18+

Brighton Journalist Works, in partnership with Brighton's daily newspaper The Argus, offer a 14-week NCTJ Diploma in Journalism. The NCTJ qualification is your stepping stone to a job in the industry and is what most UK editors require you to have. The course trains you for newspapers, magazines and online, and prepares you for jobs as a reporter and as a sub-editor. It is a multi-media journalism course which teaches you everything you need to become a journalist – researching and writing stories and features, sub-editing, video production and shorthand, as well as the essential law and public affairs modules. Students have access to unpublicised jobs and internships, and are guaranteed three weeks' work experience. You will learn from experienced working journalists in a friendly, fun and professional environment.

Twitter: @journalistworks

Web: **www.journalistworks.co.uk**

British Science Association 5-19

The British Science Association organises British Science Week every March, with over 4,500 scientific, engineering and technology events occurring throughout the country and the British Science Festival in September, which includes dialogue events for 14 to 19-year-olds. The Association also runs the nationally recognised CREST Awards, a project-based award scheme for STEM subjects. Information is sent direct to schools, and more details can be found on the website.

Twitter: @Britsciassociat

Web: **www.britishscienceassociation.org**

Cactus Language   All ages

Cactus Language help over 15,000 people every year learn more than 30 languages, in 60 countries and 500 destinations worldwide. They provide thousands of different courses around the world and can create or tailor any programme specifically to individual needs. Cactus also provide courses for children, under-18s, families and the over-50s. There is the opportunity to learn Spanish in Buenos Aires or Italian in Florence. They also offer TEFL courses for those who wish to teach English abroad.

Countries: Worldwide

Twitter: @cactuslanguage

Web: **www.cactuslanguage.com**

Central Saint Martins, University of the Arts   16-18

Take a short course in art and design at one of Britain's most revered art institutions. The courses are available over weekends, or during the Easter, Summer and Christmas holidays. Subjects include Fashion and Textiles, Fine Art, Graphic Design, Interdisciplinary, Media Arts, Theatre and Performance, and Three Dimensional Design. Fundamental to study at the College are experimentation, innovation, risk-taking, questioning and discovery, within a highly supportive learning environment, no matter which discipline you choose to study.

Twitter: @csmshortcourses

Web: **www.arts.ac.uk/csm/courses/short-courses**

CESA Languages Abroad   16+

If you want to learn Spanish in Spain or Latin America, attend a French course in France or Guadeloupe, study Italian in Italy, or do a German course in Germany or Austria, CESA have a course to suit you! You can learn Portuguese in Portugal, Japanese in Japan, Russian in Russia, Chinese in China or Arabic in Morocco. Whether you are looking for a Summer School course, are planning a Gap Year, want Exam preparation courses or are looking to combine learning a language and activities, there's a wealth of language courses abroad to choose from. There are language courses to suit all ages and abilities.

Countries: Worldwide

Twitter: @CESALanguages

Web: **www.cesalanguages.com**

don Quijote   18+

Travel to Spain or Latin America with don Quijote and learn Spanish at one of their friendly schools. Choose from a wide variety of Spanish courses. You can combine Spanish language lessons with a variety of activities, from dance practice to cooking classes. Don Quijote schools are a great place to meet new people. As well as gaining an invaluable knowledge of the Spanish language, you will inevitably come away with a new group of friends from all over the world.

Countries: Argentina, Bolivia, Chile, Costa Rica, Cuba, Dominican Republic, Ecuador, Guatemala, Mexico, Peru, Spain

Twitter: @don_Quijote

Web: **www.donquijote.co.uk**

Cordon Bleu Culinary Skills 18+

Le Cordon Bleu is a world-renowned network of educational institutions dedicated to providing the highest level of culinary and hospitality instruction through world-class programmes. You might try the four-week 'Essentials Course' at the institute's London School, or you could consider a short course at one of its centres in France, Canada, Japan, Australia, Mexico or South Korea. Le Cordon Bleu is considered to be the guardian of French culinary technique through its culinary programmes that continue to preserve and pass on the mastery and appreciation of the culinary arts that have been the cornerstone of French gastronomy for over 500 years.

Twitter: @lcbeurope

Web: **www.cordonbleu.edu**

Edinburgh School of Food and Wine 16+

Among a wide range of courses, you may be particularly interested in the Edinburgh School's four-week intensive certificate course, designed to help you earn your keep during a gap year. This practical course will give you the fundamental skills needed to cook for, say, a ski chalet or a highland lodge, and a grounding in cookery for life. Also highly relevant is the one-week 'survival course', designed to develop your culinary talents through a combination of demonstration and practical sessions. The six-month Diploma is the School's flagship course, popular with school leavers looking to learn about the culinary world, not to mention the opportunity of job prospects at the end of the course.

Twitter: @ESFW

Web: **www.esfw.com**

Embryo Veterinary School, Devon 17+

The Embryo team of experienced vets and academics offers a three-day course for aspiring vets, giving detailed analysis of Veterinary Science degree courses and honest insight into the realities of the job. Set in rural Devon, the course provides an opportunity to spend time in a working veterinary practice environment.

Twitter: @embryovets

Web: **www.embryovets.com**

ESL - Language Travel 18+

ESL offer language courses in over 200 locations around the world. Whatever your level, whether you want to learn Spanish, French, Italian, German, Chinese or any of the many other languages on offer, ESL can assist with everything from accommodation and flights to visa applications and course enrolment. With ESL's Gap Year programme, you can learn a language to an excellent standard while fully immersed in a new culture. The programmes last from 3 months and are tailor made according to your needs and objectives by their experienced language travel consultants. ESL can also arrange voluntary work, internships and paid work in your destination.

Countries: Worldwide

Twitter: @esllanguagesuk

Web: **www.esl.co.uk**

European Union Youth Orchestra 14-24

The Orchestra is made up of players representing all the member countries of the European Union (EU). The players are selected each year from over 4,000 candidates aged up to 24, who take part in auditions throughout the EU. Once the members have been selected for the year, you are invited to join the Orchestra to rehearse and perform major works on international stages all over the world.

Twitter: **@EUYOtweets**

Web: **www.euyo.org.uk**

Headstart Courses 16+

Headstart is a well-established education programme whose aim is to encourage students interested in mathematics, science or engineering to consider technology-based careers. It provides an opportunity for you in Year 12/S5 to spend up to a week at university prior to making your UCAS application.

Twitter: @TheEDTUK

Web: **www.etrust.org.uk/headstart**

John Hall Venice   16+

John Hall offers a nine-week pre-university introduction to some of the most thought-provoking achievements in the Western world, from the classical past to today. A week in London introduces themes which are developed in Venice (6 weeks). Optionally, this is followed by a week in Florence and a week in Rome. The course is conducted through on-site visits and a series of lectures by a team of world-class experts; it includes not only art, but also music, world cinema and literature. There are also practical classes offered in studio life drawing and portraiture, photography, cookery and Italian language.

Twitter: @johnhallvenice

Web: **www.johnhallvenice.com**

Jonathan Markson Tennis   10+

A graduate of Christ Church College, Oxford, Jonathan Markson is a former captain and coach of the Oxford University 'blues' tennis team and an international player for Scotland. His company offers tennis holidays and tennis camps in England, Portugal, Spain, Italy, Cyprus, South Africa, Tunisia, Mauritius and the USA (Florida). The camps aim to provide players of all ages and levels with a rewarding and enjoyable tennis experience, where the coaching is serious but fun.

Twitter: @JM_Tennis

Web: **www.marksontennis.com**

KLC School of Design   18+

The one week 'Interior Design: The Essentials' at the KLC studios in Chelsea gives an insight into the processes involved with interior design. The approach is practical, with a combination of lectures and workshops that demonstrate how to plan a room layout and how to create a stylish design by developing ideas from a basic concept. Also popular is the one-week 'Garden Design: The Essentials', held at the KLC studios in Hampton Court Palace.

Twitter: @KLCSchool

Web: **www.klc.co.uk**

Language Courses Abroad   All ages

If you are interested in learning Spanish in Spain, studying French in France, doing an Italian course in Italy, German course in Germany, or want to learn Portuguese, Russian, Arabic, Chinese, Japanese or Greek, Language Courses Abroad offer a course and location which could suit your needs and interests. They also offer combination courses, such as skiing and snowboarding in the snow-capped mountains of Europe, Canada or South America with French, German or Spanish language. Or you can give back to the local community whilst totally immersing yourself in the language and culture of the region on a language programme combined with volunteer work.

Countries: Worldwide

Web: **www.languagesabroad.co.uk**

Leiths School of Food and Wine, London   13+

This leading UK cooking school offers a range of courses for professional cooks and enthusiast amateurs. 'One Week Cookery Bootcamp' offers a fun-packed introduction to cooking and is perfect for those with a passion for food and entertaining and ideal for those heading to sixth form or university. The course is filled with practical tips and techniques for the budding chef, from baking the ultimate brownies to the perfect Sunday roast. Other courses include 'Let's Cook! Cookery Toolbox for Teenagers' for 13 to 17-year-olds and a range of one-day teenager classes in the summer.

Twitter: @Leithscooking

Web: **www.leiths.com**

London College of Fashion, University of the Arts   14-18

London College of Fashion has designed a programme of short courses and residential summer schools, allowing students to experiment with new techniques, build confidence, acquire new skills and be inspired to learn more. Short courses also take place in Dubai each February, May and October.

Twitter: @LCFLondon

Web: **www.arts.ac.uk/fashion/courses/short-courses**

National Association of Youth Theatres   14 to adult

The Association supports the development of youth theatre activity through training, advocacy, participation programmes and information services. It lists training and events and gives details of youth theatres in your area. There are six associate venues working in partnership with NAYT who produce an annual festival for young people. Each festival is a day-long event and is packed with workshops and performances. See the website for information.

Twitter: @nayttweets

Web: **www.nayt.org.uk**

National Student Drama Festival   16-25

The National Student Drama Festival features performances, workshops, discussions, masterclasses and entertainment. The Festival is a seven-day celebration of young people's theatre and features the best of British work alongside exceptional productions by young people from across the world. It is for anyone who wants to get involved with drama and the creative industries and is a place where the most inspirational work from diverse, young and emerging artists is celebrated and presented alongside workshops from leading professionals from around the world.

Twitter: @nsdfest

Web: **www.nsdf.org.uk**

National Youth Orchestra of Great Britain 13-19

One of the world's finest youth orchestras, the National Youth Orchestra (NYO) draws together each year 160-plus talented musicians, aged up to 19, from all over the UK. The orchestra meets during the school holidays for intensive two-week periods of coaching and rehearsal with leading professional musicians and some of the world's finest conductors and soloists, before performing in iconic concert halls such as Symphony Hall, Birmingham, The Sage Gateshead and the Royal Albert Hall.

Twitter: @nyotweets

Web: **www.nyo.org.uk**

National Youth Orchestras of Scotland 8-25

The National Youth Orchestras of Scotland is unique in providing complete orchestral experience for its students aged between 8 and 25, through its comprehensive range of orchestras and training ensembles. NYOS organises training, intensive rehearsals and national and international concert tours. NYOS is committed to introducing musical experiences to all of Scotland's young people.

Twitter: @NYOScotland

Web: **www.nyos.co.uk**

Nick Nairn Cook School, Scotland 16+

TV chef Nick Nairn is the man behind the Nick Nairn Cook School, a foodie haven built around a single objective: teaching kitchen confidence. The cook school offers a variety of courses where visitors can pick up new skills, inspiration and knowledge all whilst preparing their own gourmet lunch. There are two schools: one hidden away in the foothills of the Trossachs, right at the heart of some of Scotland's finest scenery; and the other, their new urban cook school located in Aberdeen.

Twitter: @thecookschool

Web: **www.nicknairncookschool.com**

OISE 7-17

OISE Young Learners courses give children and teenagers a head start in life by equipping them with the English language skills necessary to succeed in this modern and multilingual world. Lessons are designed to develop accuracy, encourage confidence and fluency, and are taught in small groups with a maximum of eight students per class. Lessons range from beginner to advanced level. As part of a fully immersed experience, students also have the opportunity to participate in an exciting social and activity programme, which enables them to continue their learning outside of the classroom whilst making friends and relaxing after an action-packed day.

Countries: Australia, Canada, UK, USA

Twitter: @OISE_English

Web: **www.oise.com**

Medlink   16+

Medlink is a three- to five-day course for young people considering a career in medicine. It gives delegates the opportunity to discuss medical school admissions and careers in medicine with Deans from a number of medical schools, as well as advice on surviving medical school given by medical students. It also provides the chance to talk with practising doctors and medical students. The course is valuable for students in years 12 and 13.

Twitter: @medlinkteam

Web: http://medlink-uk.net

Medsim   16+

Medsim is a two- or three-day residential course held at the Nottingham University School of Medicine. Medsim offers a rich selection of patient contact and practicals that will considerably strengthen your UCAS application. Most importantly, the experience of working under supervision in small groups, with real patients and equipment, has the benefit of allowing you to experience what it is like to be a doctor, to deal with patients, to be on-call and to work under pressure.

Web: **www.workshop-uk.net/medsim**

Pre-Med Course   16+

Pre-Med Course is a one-day medical careers course run by a team of doctors. The course gives impartial careers information to anyone considering medicine as a career. Topics covered include application procedures, interviews, medical school curriculum, and practical demonstrations. Courses are normally held in September, December and April of each year.

Web: **www.premed.org.uk**

News Associates   18+

Based in London and Manchester, News Associates offer NCTJ-accredited courses in Journalism. The 20-week 'Fast Track' course covers reporting, portfolio, shorthand, law, public affairs and either sport or sub-editing. With a packed timetable and 40-hour weeks, it is not for the faint-hearted! News Associates holds free monthly workshops when those interested in journalism training can try simulated news exercises.

Twitter: @NewsAssociates

Web: **http://newsassociates.co.uk**

Orchards Cookery, Worcestershire 16+

This award-winning cookery school won Cookery School of the Year in 2013 and was also Best English Cookery School. The one- and two-week 'Chalet Cooks' courses can show you how to master the art of being a great chalet cook, enabling you to get the most out of a gap year job in the mountains. The school also offers a recruitment service, helping students with CV writing, interview training and so on. Alternatively, the five-day 'Off to University' course covers healthy, delicious and affordable meals for students, including easy entertaining.

Twitter: @OrchardsCookery

Web: **www.orchardscookery.co.uk**

Oxford Media and Business School 17+

The School's 'Gap Year Life Skills' course is designed to give you an early taste of a university-style environment, together with training in key Life Skills such as the use of the latest IT software. The Careers Direct placement bureau will then help you find temping work, which can be invaluable both for later university submissions and for earning cash to fund the rest of your Gap Year.

Web: **www.oxfordbusiness.co.uk/gap.html**

Padstow Seafood School, Cornwall 15-16

TV chef Rick Stein's famous cooking school mostly caters for adults, but does offer half-day courses for students during the Easter and summer holidays. For both those who've never cooked with fish and seafood enthusiasts alike, the half-day course teaches you the techniques you'll need in order to create really impressive fish dishes.

Twitter: @TheSeafood

Web: **www.rickstein.com**

Pitman Training 17+

Pitman training offer flexible, self-paced training, which is tailor made to fit around current work commitments and lifestyle. Courses are available in areas such as IT and Business skills, including Bookkeeping and Accounts, Web Design, Shorthand, Spreadsheets and Word Processing.

Countries: Gibraltar, Jersey, Kuwait, Mauritius, Spain, UK

Twitter: @PitmanTraining

Web: **www.pitman-training.com**

Press Association Training   18+

Press Association Training offer NCTJ-accredited courses in multi-media journalism. The courses are based in London, at the Press Association's headquarters, or in Newcastle in the offices of the publishers of the Evening Chronicle, Journal and Sunday Sun. The 17-week full-time course runs twice a year, in spring and autumn. You'll learn all the basics of being a great reporter and have the chance to produce stories for the Evening Chronicle, The Journal and the Sunday Sun on the Newcastle course, and various London newspapers if you are studying in the capital.

Twitter: @PA_Training

Web: **www.becomeareporter.co.uk**

Quest Professional   16+

Quest Professional offers practical business skills training to school leavers and university graduates looking to get the skills that employers want and fill in the gaps on their CV. You will develop your practical office IT skills and business communication, as well as increasing your commercial awareness and knowledge of marketing, management, business finance, social and digital media. Throughout the training programmes, you will focus on your future career, CV, job hunting and interview skills technique.

Twitter: @QuestLondon

Web: **www.questprofessional.co.uk**

Royal Institution   All ages

An important part of the work of the Royal Institution is to promote an understanding of science in young people. To further this aim, lectures, events and summer schools are held specifically targeted at the new generation of budding scientists.

Twitter: @ri_science

Web: **www.rigb.org**

Salters' Chemistry Camps   14-16

These are popular three-day residential Camps, held at universities throughout the UK and packed with exciting chemistry and social events. The aim of the Camps is to encourage young people to participate in the fun of chemistry and motivate them to develop awareness of and a long-term interest in the subject.

Twitter: @Salters_Inst

Web: **www.saltersinstitute.co.uk/camps**

Smallpeice Trust — 12-17

The Smallpeice Trust is an independent charity that works to encourage more young people to consider a career in Science, Technology, Engineering and Maths. As part of this, the Trust offers three- to five-day residential courses to provide students with a real-life insight into various strands of engineering. Students in Years 8-12 are offered the opportunity to work with leading engineering companies at top universities around the country, in areas such as Biochemical Engineering, Nuclear Engineering and Physics in Engineering.

Twitter:	@SmallpeiceTrust

Web:	**www.smallpeicetrust.org.uk**

Tante Marie Culinary Academy, Surrey — 16+

Renowned for its professional Diploma courses, Tante Marie offers three shorter courses particularly suited to readers of this book. Whether you are keen to go for a gap year job in a stunning location, would like to take your culinary skills to a higher level or just want a short introduction to cooking well for yourself, family and friends, there could be a suitable course for you. The one-term 'Cordon Bleu Certificate' is highly valued by ski companies and other gap year employers, although you might also consider the four-week 'Essential Skills' course. If you simply want to eat well at university, look at the one- or two-week 'Beginners' courses, offering an introduction to good food and healthy eating.

Twitter:	@TanteMarie

Web:	**www.tantemarie.co.uk**

Up To Speed Journalism   18+

Since 2006, Up To Speed have been running courses for aspiring journalists. The courses are designed by professional journalists and photographers and taught by professionals who have worked at the top in British media. Up To Speed journalists have gone on to work in every area of the profession, from newspapers to magazines and from broadcasting to online news. Courses are accredited by the National Council for the Training of Journalists (NCTJ) and held in a newspaper building.

Twitter: @Up_To_Speed

Web: **http://uptospeedjournalism.co.uk**

Workshop Conferences   16+

Workshop Conferences offer short residential courses, covering such career/degree-related topics as: nursing, medicine, physiotherapy, psychology, veterinary science, chemistry, physics, forensics, journalism, dentistry and law.

Twitter: @theworkshopteam

Web: **www.workshop-uk.net**

Year Out Drama Company   18+

Year Out Drama provides an intensive, practical drama course, led by experts in professionally equipped performance spaces. This is a full-time programme providing an intensive practical drama course with a theatre company feel. The course includes Acting, Directing, Design, Costume, Voice Work, Movement, Text Study, Theatre Trips and at least four full-scale performances during the year, including a production at the Edinburgh Festival.

Twitter: @YearOutDrama

Web: **www.yearoutdrama.com**

4. Treks/Expeditions and Activity Holidays

If you want to combine an adventure trek with an environmental, scientific or community project, you may find something suitable here. Expect to pay a substantial participation fee, for which you may have to raise sponsorship. Apart from being one of the best ways in which to fund your expedition, the experience of having to secure a considerable sum of money will help develop a range of skills before you even leave home! Expedition programmes give you the opportunity to develop many other important skills such as communication and time management. You will be building confidence and self-esteem, in addition to learning to lead the expedition team and taking your turn to do so. You should also meet a group of like-minded people and have a lot of fun. Whatever destination you choose, you could end up doing something that will look good on your CV and will be highly valued by universities and employers.

British Exploring   16+

British Exploring organises extreme adventure and conservation expeditions in remote, wild environments. You could find yourself monitoring climate change in the Arctic, measuring biodiversity in the jungle or investigating human impact on the environment in mountainous regions. The aim is always to develop the confidence, teamwork, leadership and spirit of adventure and exploration of all expedition members.

Twitter: @Brit_exploring

Web: **www.britishexploring.org**

Camps International   18-25

Camps International operates a permanent network of international volunteer camps in the heart of rural communities and wildlife conservation areas in Kenya, Tanzania, Borneo, Cambodia and Ecuador. Camps offer you the chance to make a difference by volunteering in over 100 community, wildlife and conservation projects, bringing revenue and assistance to rural communities that would otherwise not benefit from tourism.

Countries: Kenya, Tanzania, Borneo, Cambodia, Ecuador

Twitter: @CampsInt

Web: **www.campsinternational.com**

Dragoman Overland   18+

Dragoman has been running adventure trips for over 30 years across the four continents of Africa, Asia, North and South America. Its overland tours range from 9 to 235 days in length. The shorter two- or three-week trips offer a snapshot of a country or region, giving travellers a short, sharp adventure travel experience. A simple break from everyday life can get you off the tourist trail and take you on a perspective-changing journey. On one of the longer tours you could cover a whole continent. The iconic Istanbul to Beijing overland follows in the footsteps of the ancient Silk Road caravans, or you can join Dragoman on a trans-Africa expedition from Cape Town to Cairo.

Twitter: @DragomanTravel

Web: **www.dragoman.com**

G Adventures   18+

G Adventures arranges a range of adventure holidays around the world, giving you the opportunity to step off the beaten track and experience authentic accommodation and local transportation to bring you face to face with the world's most fascinating cultures, customs and awe-inspiring wildlife. Adventures include the Arctic and Antarctica that call out to a select breed of traveller. Are you one of them? Set sail aboard the MS Expedition and explore these harsh and unbelievably rewarding frozen frontiers. Visit North Africa and the Middle East, where holy relics, ancient ruins and other reminders of yesterday may start to explain why travellers come to this part of the world.

Twitter: @gAdventures

Web: **www.gadventures.com**

Gap Year Diver   18+

A small and independent UK-based tour operator, Gap Year Diver specialises in gap year and career break scuba diving holidays. Expeditions are designed for beginners as well as those with previous diving experience. Get involved with marine conservation, dive with sharks, explore wrecks or explore a country with adventure and diving! Examples of places with trips on offer are the Red Sea, Caribbean, South Pacific Island Retreat, Thailand, Indonesia, Venezuela and Costa Rica.

Twitter: @GapYearDiver

Web: **www.gapyeardiver.com**

Jubilee Sailing Trust   16+

The Jubilee Sailing Trust (JST) is a charity that aims to promote the integration of people of all physical abilities through the challenge and adventure of tall ship sailing. The JST owns and operates two tall ships – LORD NELSON and TENACIOUS – the only two vessels in the world that have been purpose-designed and built to enable a crew of mixed physical abilities to sail side by side on equal terms. If you take on the tall ship challenge with the JST, it could be a short hop around the British coast, a four-week transatlantic challenge, a week's island hopping in the Canary Islands or the Caribbean, or a place in the European Tall Ships' Race.

Twitter: @JubileeSailing

Web: **www.jst.org.uk**

Oasis Overland   17+

Oasis Overland is an adventure travel company with a huge number of overland trips in several continents, including Africa, the Middle East, Latin America, and long journeys across Asia. Oasis Overland trips, mostly in their purpose-built vehicles that can take up to 24 people, vary in length up to 38 weeks. Your expedition could involve anything from 9 days in Egypt to 38 weeks across Africa.

Twitter: @OasisOverland

Web: **www.oasisoverland.co.uk**

Outward Bound   11 to 19

The Outward Bound Trust runs adventure programmes ideal for young people looking to do something different with their summer. It offers a range of one-week to 19-day experiences, run throughout the summer months, including a range of specialist climbing, biking or paddling adventures. Each programme not only gives you a chance to try out new activities, from gorge scrambling to expeditions in the mountains, but also equips you with new skills and can make a real difference to your CV or university application. Choose from three locations: Loch Eil in the Scottish Highlands, Ullswater in the Lake District or Aberdovey in Snowdonia, Wales.

Twitter: @OutwardBoundUK

Web: **www.outwardbound.org.uk**

Quaystage Training · 14-25

Quaystage delivers water-based outdoor activity adventures and training. These provide a platform for experiential learning, personal development and achievement. Opportunities include Sail Camp and Dive Camp adventures during school holidays, and Tall Ship sailing adventures.

Twitter: @BritSailTrain

Web: **www.quaystage.co.uk**

Rail Adventure across Europe · All ages

InterRail offers European train passes and information on how to travel around Europe by train, including planning your journey, timetables, maps and passes. The most popular product is the InterRail Global Pass which gives you flexible train travel in 30 countries. InterRail offer a special youth discount up to the age of 25.

Countries: Austria, Belgium, Bosnia-Herzegovina, Bulgaria, Croatia, Czech Republic, Denmark, FYR Macedonia, Finland, France, Germany, Great Britain, Greece, Hungary, Ireland, Italy, Luxembourg, Montenegro, Netherlands, Norway, Poland, Portugal, Romania, Serbia, Slovakia, Slovenia, Spain, Sweden, Switzerland, Turkey.

Twitter: @InterRail

Web: **www.interrail.eu**

Raleigh International   17-24

The Raleigh overseas programme enables participants from all over the world and from all backgrounds to undertake a blend of mental and physical challenges. The full 10-week programme consists of three distinct project phases – sustainable community and environmental projects plus an adventure phase. There are also five-week programmes, which combine your choice of either a community or environmental project with a team-based adventure challenge.

Countries: Borneo, Costa Rica, India, Nicaragua, Tanzania

Twitter: @Raleigh_

Web: **www.raleighinternational.org**

Royal Geographical Society   16+

Every year the Society supports between 40 and 50 teams of students and researchers to get into the field with a Geographical Fieldwork Grant, the Society's longest-running grant scheme. The three independent travel grants support challenging and inspiring geographical journeys and expeditions and are worth up to £3,000. Full details of the different grants available can be found on the website. Fully funded places are available on a five-day fieldwork summer school for AS geography students at the end of Year 12. The courses give students who would not normally have such opportunities a chance to experience high quality residential fieldwork.

Twitter: @RGS_IBG

Web: **www.rgs.org/OurWork/Fieldwork+and+Expeditions/ Fieldwork+Expeditions.htm**

Tall Ships Adventures   16+

The Tall Ships Youth Trust is dedicated to the personal development of young people aged 12 to 25. The fleet includes Tall Ship Stavros S Niarchos, a magnificent 200ft Brig, four 72ft Challenger Yachts and the 62ft Tall Ships Catamaran. They are operated by Tall Ships and work 12 months of the year, both around the UK and abroad, offering Tall Ship Adventure Sailing Holidays. Recognised by the Duke of Edinburgh Award as an activity provider and approved for the Royal Yachting Association Competent Crew qualification.

Countries: Predominantly UK and European waters but also the Caribbean

Twitter: @TallShipsYT

Web: **http://tallships.org**

Tour Dust   18+

Tourdust is a specialist adventure tour operator for independent travellers looking to book activity holidays, adventure holidays and tours from expert local guides all around the world. Experiences offered by Tourdust include Inca Trail treks and trekking in Morocco's Atlas Mountains, alongside a host of other trips such as safaris in the Masai Mara and sea kayaking in the Aegean.

Countries: Croatia, Ecuador, Ethiopia, Greece, Kenya, Morocco, Peru, South Africa, Sweden, Tanzania, Turkey, USA

Twitter: @Tourdust

Web: **www.tourdust.com**

TrekAmerica   18+

TrekAmerica's distinctive style of adventure travel offers something different to your ordinary guided tour. It organises small group adventures across the USA, Canada, Alaska and Central America. Every year thousands of young people from all over the world find that its small group tours offer an easy and dependable way to explore North America.

Countries: Belize, Canada, Costa Rica, Guatemala, Honduras, Mexico, Nicaragua, Peru, USA

Twitter: @trekamerica

Web: **www.trekamerica.co.uk**

Trekforce Extreme Expeditions   18+

With over 20 years' experience of organising expeditions – that combine real adventure with a serious purpose – in the rainforests, deserts and mountains of the world, Trekforce runs one- to five-month expeditions and gap year programmes that tackle tough conservation or development projects, and can be followed by intensive language courses and long-term teaching placements in rural communities. It also offers a series of two- to three-week Extreme Expeditions to the most testing environments around the world, designed to push you to the very limit.

Twitter: @gapforce

Web: **www.trekforce.org.uk**

VentureCo   17-20

VentureCo's multi-phase travel programmes incorporate development projects, expeditions and adventure travel in Asia, Africa and South America. The ventures are a combination of complementary phases. For example, in South America you would combine a Spanish language phase with a Project phase and an Expedition phase to make one venture. Each phase reveals a different aspect of your host country and together they produce one memorable travel experience. Participation in the venture is the most important element of its success: venturers are team players with considerable input into the everyday running of each phase.

Countries: Argentina, Bolivia, Botswana, Chile, DR Congo, Ecuador, Ethiopia, Guyana, India, Kenya, Malawi, Morocco, Mozambique, Nepal, Peru, Rwanda, Tanzania, Uganda, Zambia, Zimbabwe

Twitter: @VentureCoUK

Web: **www.ventureco-worldwide.com**

Wind, Sand and Stars   16-23

Wind, Sand and Stars are desert specialists. Working closely with local tribal communities they offer authentic, personal and close-up experiences. The trips have combined desert adventures, mountain treks, camel safaris, field trips, school journeys, silent retreats, pilgrimage to historical religious sites, charity projects and more. Whether travelling through the deserts of Arabia or highlands of Ethiopia, they have built strong working relationships with the local people who offer you their warm hospitality and an insight into their traditional ways of life.

Countries: Egypt, Ethiopia, Oman, Jordan

Twitter: @Wind_Sand_Stars

Web: **www.windsandstars.co.uk**

Woodlarks Campsite Trust   16+

Situated in twelve acres of beautiful Surrey countryside, Woodlarks Campsite enables children and adults with disabilities to enjoy a host of activities they may never have thought possible. Woodlarks camps can be as tranquil or as adventurous as you want them to be.

Twitter: @WoodlarksCamp

Web: **www.woodlarks.org.uk**

Yamnuska Mountain Adventures   17+

Yamnuska Mountain Adventures is a mountain skills and experience organisation. Courses are led by experienced mountain guides and instructors. The company specialises in Mountaineering, Rock Climbing, Ice Climbing, Ski Touring, Trekking and Avalanche education at beginner to expert level. The Three Month Mountain Skills and Leadership Semester based in Alberta, Canada gives participants the skills and experiences for safe mountain travel and leadership. Yamnuska arranges your accommodation for the whole trip and provides all meals when you are out in the field.

Countries: Canada

Twitter: @Yamnuska_Mt_Adv

Web: **www.yamnuska.com/climbing-school**

Yomps   All ages

Yomps provide suggestions for outdoor activity holidays for adults, families, school trips, college trips and young people from across the continent and beyond. They recommend the remote Brecon Beacons of Wales, a wild landscape that is perfect for adventure, finding new things and exploration. If you want to take part in a specialist or many-activity break that involves Walking, Abseiling, Land Yachting, Orienteering, Rock Climbing, Sea Kayaking, Climbing, Surfing, Survival and many more things for a week, a weekend or a day, then Yomps may be able to help.

Twitter: @Yomps

Web: **www.yomps.co.uk**

5. Industry/Employment

Learn how business works...and get paid for it in some cases! You may be carrying out research, designing prototypes, planning projects, handling customers' needs or devising new working methods. Projects vary depending on company needs.

Aviva Work Experience Opportunities   16-18+

The sixth largest insurance company in the world, Aviva offers work experience opportunities in cities throughout the UK. All placements are advertised through the Directions online careers service for the financial and legal sectors. You can register with Directions via the link below.

Web: **www.careers.aviva.co.uk**

Web: **http://register.directions.org.uk**

BBC   14-18+

The British Broadcasting Corporation has work experience placements available in just about every area of BBC activity across the UK. Whatever your age and whichever area you're interested in, there could be something right for you, from advertising, charitable work or entertaining to journalism, music or the World Service. All placements are unpaid and can last anything from a few days to four weeks. Competition is fierce, so before you apply you'll need to consider what you can offer and what you'd like to achieve. Are you good with computers? Have you worked in hospital radio or written articles for your local or college magazine? What do you hope to gain from the placement? What are your ambitions for the future? These are the kinds of questions you should be asking yourself.

Twitter: @bbcrecruitment

Web: **www.bbc.co.uk/careers/work7-experience**

BDO Summer School   Year 12

BDO LLP, one of the UK's largest accountancy and business advisory firms, offers a two-week programme, during which you will go out on real client assignments, will gain exposure to a variety of industry sectors and will interact with a wide range of senior people, including partners and managers. You must be in Year 12 to be eligible, with Grade B or above in GCSE Maths and English, and predicted to achieve 280 UCAS Points at A level or equivalent.

Web: **www.bdoschoolleavers.co.uk/Summer-School-programme**

Engineering Education Scheme   16-17

The engineering education scheme gives young people the opportunity to work on a real-life engineering project with a leading organisation across six months. Students work with company mentors to develop employability skills that will help them in their future studies and careers.

Twitter: @TheEDTUK

Web: **www.etrust.org.uk/engineering-education-scheme**

Gap Medics   16-25

Gap Medics specialises in medical work experience projects. Its one-to eight-week placements offer aspiring medics an invaluable insight into working in a hospital environment. Students spend at least 23 hours per week shadowing doctors and other healthcare professionals. They also have the opportunity to attend global health tutorials, where doctors from local hospitals provide seminars on local and national health issues. All students stay in custom-built Gap Medics houses. Evenings and weekends are filled with activities such as safaris, hill tribe treks and social barbecues.

Countries: Czech Republic, Tanzania, Thailand

Twitter: @GapMedics

Web: **www.gapmedics.co.uk**

GlaxoSmithKline   16-18

Leading research-based pharmaceutical and healthcare company GlaxoSmithKline offers an annual work experience programme at its research and development sites in Stevenage, Ware and Harlow during the February half term. It is a week packed with interesting experiences. During your week with them, you learn by doing – on the job – and you can pick up some handy tips from the experienced colleagues around you. Places are available to students in Year 12/13 studying science, IT or engineering. Please note priority is given to students attending schools that are local to the Stevenage, Ware and Harlow areas.

Twitter: @GSK

Web: **www.gsk.com/uk/careers/school-students.html**

HSBC   14-18

HSBC Bank runs a one-week structured programme for 14 to 18-year-olds aimed at providing an exposure to the financial services industry. You'll experience what it is like to work in retail, commercial, operational or head office areas. This will help you decide if you like banking as a career and whether you should join before or after university.

Twitter: @HSBC_UK_Careers

Web: **http://jobs.hsbc.co.uk/apprentices/work-experience-programme.aspx**

John Lewis Partnership   16-17+

John Lewis offers an opportunity to spend two weeks in a department store, where you can gain an insight into the world of retailing. Placements are normally in selling departments but John Lewis can also accommodate students in other areas of the business if you have a particular interest.

Twitter: @johnlewisretail

Web: **www.jlpjobs.com**

PGL   18+

PGL provides children's adventure holidays and educational courses at its 24 activity centres across the UK, France and Spain. Every year it recruits over 2,500 staff to instruct, inspire and look after its guests, with vacancies for watersports instructors, adventure activity instructors, group leaders, language speakers, TEFL Teachers, administrators, maintenance, catering and domestic staff. There are also ad hoc ski rep positions for the peak weeks of the winter operating season.

Countries: UK, France, Spain

Twitter: @pglstaff

Web: **www.pgl.co.uk/jobs**

Pinsent Masons   16-18

Pinsent Masons lawyers offer a number of week-long placements across their network of UK offices: Birmingham, Leeds, London and Manchester in England; Aberdeen, Edinburgh and Glasgow in Scotland; or Belfast in Northern Ireland. You will need to be already studying towards either AS or A Levels, or equivalent qualifications. During your week at the firm you will take part in a business exercise, attend information presentations and seminars in addition to shadowing lawyers on real issues. You will spend time in a number of different departments and will be supervised by a trainee solicitor, who will help you gain an appreciation of the skills you need to be a good lawyer.

Twitter: @PinsentMasons

Web: **www.pinsentmasons.com/en/careers/work-experience**

PwC Business Insight Week   Year 12

If you are considering a career in business, you can spend a week in a PwC office of your choice during your summer holiday. In addition to developing your employability skills, you will see how PwC advises household brands and global companies on everything from planning for the future to how they can make best use of their technology.

Twitter: @PwC_UK_Careers

Web: **www.pcw.co.uk/careers/schools/flying-start-degrees/business-insight-week.jhtml**

Year in Industry   17+

The Year in Industry scheme offers paid, degree-relevant work placements in a year out before or during your university course. With opportunities in all branches of science, technology, engineering, maths and business management, you can undertake real projects and learn how business works. The skills you develop should enhance your university education and maximise your graduate job prospects. Many companies view the scheme as an important part of their recruitment programme, and go on to sponsor placement students through university.

Twitter: @TheEDTUK

Web: **www.etrust.org.uk/year_in_industry.cfm**

6. Nature/Conservation

Projects listed here are for those with a particular passion for wildlife and conservation, although some schemes involve the preservation of buildings. Costs vary from nothing to several thousand pounds. The inspiration for many current conservation projects came from the 'Earth Summit' held in Rio de Janeiro in 1992. This was followed up with the United Nations Conference on Sustainable Development in 2012, also held in Rio and commonly known as Rio+20 or Rio Earth Summit 2012. The initial event was the first global recognition of the urgent need to preserve the diversity of life on earth, culminating in a resolve by 168 countries present to undertake biodiversity surveys of their 'at threat' regions. Many countries committing to this pledge needed assistance with funding and personnel to complete these surveys, leading them to invite some of the organisations listed below to undertake the necessary work. Long-term survival for humans on earth depends on protecting the diversity of organisms, each of which plays a part in maintaining the planet's critical functions.

African Conservation Experience   17+

African Conservation Experience claims to be one of the most experienced organisations for conservation placements in Southern Africa. It can offer you the chance to work on game and nature reserves alongside conservationists, zoologists, wildlife vets and reserve managers. The organisation welcomes volunteers from all backgrounds, with no previous experience necessary, from the age of 17 upwards. Volunteer Placements are from two weeks to three months, and you can combine two or more projects in one trip. You could join a placement as part of a gap year, in a summer break from school or university, or as part of a career break or sabbatical.

Countries: Botswana, Mauritius, South Africa, Zimbabwe

Twitter: @AfricanConsExp

Web: **www.conservationafrica.net**

Blue Ventures   17+

A not-for-profit organisation dedicated to facilitating projects and expeditions that enhance global marine conservation and research, Blue Ventures coordinates expeditions consisting of scientists and volunteers, working hand-in-hand with local biologists, governmental departments and communities, to carry out research, environmental awareness and conservation programmes at threatened marine habitats around the world.

Countries: Belize, Madagascar

Twitter: @BlueVentures

Web: **www.blueventures.org**

Coral Cay Conservation   18+ (16+ if a school group)

Coral Cay Conservation (CCC) is a not-for-profit marine conservation organisation, sending teams of volunteers to survey some of the world's most endangered coral reefs and tropical forests. Its mission is to protect these crucial environments by working closely with the local communities who depend on them for food and livelihood. CCC currently has a marine expedition in the Philippines, and a terrestrial and marine expedition in Montserrat. The organisation is financed through a combination of grants, and volunteers who pay to participate in an expedition for anything from one week upwards. Volunteers do not need to have any science or dive training as all of the necessary training is covered on site.

Countries: Montserrat, Philippines

Twitter: @CoralCay

Web: **www.coralcay.org**

Earthwatch   15-18

Earthwatch Teen Expeditions are designed specifically and exclusively for 15 to 18-year-olds. Working with projects all around the world, they're hands-on, engaging and meaningful – providing unrivalled opportunities to undertake vital, peer-reviewed scientific field research under the supervision of skilled research teams in a professional setting. Whether you're interested in helping conserve the Amazon Basin's pink river dolphins, snorkel and survey reefs in Belize, or dig for cultural treasures of a Roman villa, Earthwatch has an expedition for you.

Twitter: @earthwatch_org

Web: **www.earthwatch.org**

Frontier   17+

Frontier is a non-profit conservation and development organisation dedicated to safeguarding biodiversity and ecosystem integrity and building sustainable livelihoods for marginalised communities in the world's poorest countries. It hosts a myriad of global conservation projects, offering 'hands-on' fieldwork, which benefits endangered tropical wildlife and their ecosystems and directly assists developing countries rich in biodiversity but poor in the capacity to manage natural resources.

Countries: Worldwide

Twitter: @FrontierGap

Web: **www.frontier.ac.uk**

Greenforce   17+

Much of Greenforce's current activity is focused on conserving coral reefs. Widely known as the rainforests of the sea, the reefs are home to a massive diversity of species and are much more than just a pretty underwater garden for divers to enjoy. On land, the competition for living space and resources is pushing wildlife into ever shrinking zones. Another major part of the work that Greenforce does is to contribute to improving the lives of fragile and threatened communities, such as the Maasai in parts of Tanzania, and the Quichua Indians deep in the Amazon jungle.

Countries: Australia, Bahamas, Belize, Borneo, Botswana, China, Ecuador, Fiji, Galápagos Islands, Ghana, Guatemala, India, Namibia, Nepal, Peru, South Africa, Tanzania, Zambia, Zimbabwe

Twitter: @gapforce

Web: **www.greenforce.org**

Worldwide Experience   17+

Worldwide Experience allows you to work with animals while contributing to global conservation and community programmes. It specialises in conservation projects in Southern Africa but also offers animal rehabilitation projects, veterinary experiences, school groups and game ranger courses. Other activities can include sports coaching and teaching, marine conservation, wildlife photography and filmmaking. All projects are run by specialists in their field who are specifically trained to impart their skills and experience. For example a two-week programme working on a conservation project somewhere in Southern Africa, where you assist in the work of an award-winning conservation team, costs from £709 per person.

Twitter: @WorldwideExp

Web: **www.worldwideexperience.com**

Worldwide Opportunities on Organic Farms   17+

A network of organisations covering some 100 countries, WWOOF arranges volunteer work on organic farms across the world, from Afghanistan to Zambia. In return for volunteer help and a small fee, food, accommodation and opportunities to learn about organic lifestyles are provided. Usually you live with your host and are expected to join in and cooperate with the day-to-day activities. In most countries the exchange is based on 4-6 hours help-fair exchange for a full day's food and accommodation. You may be asked to help with a variety of tasks like sowing seed, making compost, gardening, planting, cutting wood, weeding, harvesting, packing, milking, feeding, fencing, making mud-bricks, wine making, cheese making and bread making. Most WWOOF visits are between one and two weeks, though some may be as short as two or three days or as long as six months.

Twitter: @WWOOF

Web: **www.wwoof.net**

7. Community Projects in the UK

In this section, you may be able to live at home and work on a local volunteer project, while some schemes insist that being away from home is an essential part of the gap year experience.

Community Service Volunteers   18-35

The UK's largest volunteering and training organisation, CSV provides hundreds of full-time volunteering opportunities across the UK that will equip you with life skills and enhance your CV or UCAS application. You will spend 6-12 months living away from home, supporting people in need and enabling them to develop or manage their own lives. As a CSV volunteer you will take on an important role that is valued by the community. You can use your skills and develop new ones, test yourself out in new situations, challenge your way of thinking, and make a genuine and positive impact on people's lives. CSV's placements are community-based, supporting a wide variety of people. You may be helping people with physical disabilities or learning difficulties, or supporting elderly people, children or young people.

Twitter: @CSV_UK

Web: **www.csv.org.uk**

CSV Heritage Camps   16-25

Experience the hidden history of some of Britain's oldest and most beautiful buildings. Cathedrals, abbeys, minsters, chapels and parish churches make up a huge part of Britain's architectural heritage and every year teams of young people from all over the world move in to help refresh and conserve these buildings. CSV's Heritage Camps programme has been running week-long residential breaks at cathedrals and churches throughout the UK for over 30 years – there are on average 20 camps at different venues, running each year throughout July and August.

Twitter: @CSV_UK

Web: **www.csv.org.uk/heritage-camps**

Do-it
All ages

The Do-it website is a volunteering database run by charity IVO. The search works on locations, just enter your postcode or town to find opportunities in your area and search through one million opportunities to volunteer and apply online. The majority of opportunities available come from local Volunteer Centres.

Twitter: @doituk

Web: **www.do-it.org.uk**

National Trust
All ages

If you don't want to travel too far but are still looking for a way to make a difference in conserving the environment and the UK's heritage, the National Trust could have something to offer. As a volunteer, you can learn new skills and meet new people while working right at the heart of beautiful buildings, gardens and landscapes. The Trust also runs around 450 Working Holidays every year throughout England, Wales and Northern Ireland, where you could be involved with anything from carrying out a conservation survey to herding goats, painting a lighthouse or planting trees.

Twitter: @nationaltrust

Web: **www.nationaltrust.org.uk/get-involved**

National Trust for Scotland   16+

The National Trust for Scotland offers plenty of volunteering opportunities in the heritage sector. It also organises week-long residential working holidays at NT Thistle Camps, where you can get involved in conserving the historic locations under its care. Campers can live and work in some of Scotland's most remarkable and remote places. Whilst Thistle camps are for over-18s, the trust also runs Trailblazer camps for 16 and 17-year-olds.

Twitter: @N_T_S

Web: **www.nts.org.uk/Volunteering**

The Prince's Trust   13-30

The Prince's Trust helps young people overcome barriers and get their lives working. Through practical support including training, mentoring and financial assistance, the Trust helps 13 to 30-year-olds realise their potential and transform their lives. The main target groups are those who have struggled at school, been in care, been in trouble with the law, or are long-term unemployed.

Twitter: @PrincesTrust

Web: **www.princes-trust.org.uk**

Reach   Adult

Not aimed primarily at school or college leavers, Reach seeks to match the skills of experienced people to the needs of voluntary organisations. Reach recruits and supports people with managerial, technical and professional expertise and places them in part-time, unpaid roles in voluntary organisations that need their help. Volunteers are placed with organisations near where they live, anywhere in the UK.

Twitter: @ReachSkills

Web: **www.reachskills.org.uk**

vInspired   14-25

vInspired helps you discover the value of volunteering – for yourself and for others. It offers fun, easy-to-access opportunities to get you excited about doing good things. Its online market-place and mobile apps link you with interesting and varied opportunities with almost 2,000 charities across the country. The innovative programmes provide structured support for you to do good and gain new skills in your own way, while earning vInspired Awards to illuminate your CV. Whether you have never volunteered before, or are a veteran volunteer, whether you have an hour or a week to give, vInspired has a project or opportunity for you.

Twitter: @vinspired

Web: **www.vInspired.com**

8. Teaching/Coaching

Projects listed here focus mainly on teaching English or sports and outdoor activities. You may even get paid, especially if you can offer specific coaching qualifications (e.g. in swimming, canoeing etc), although you must pay to participate in some schemes.

IST Plus   17+

With an IST Plus cultural exchange programme you can work, study, travel or teach in locations throughout the world. Work in the USA, teach in Thailand or China, travel around Australia and New Zealand and Singapore, or study a language anywhere in the world.

Countries: Australia, Cambodia, China, New Zealand, Singapore, Thailand, USA

Twitter: @ISTPlusWorld

Web: **www.istplus.com**

Flying Fish   17+

Flying Fish trains and recruits over 1000 people each year to work as yacht skippers and as sailing, diving, surfing, windsurfing and ski and snowboard instructors. As an experienced yacht skipper or instructor, you can then spend time earning money from your favourite sport. Courses range from one week to 19 weeks and are available to complete beginners and for those who already have some experience.

Twitter: @FlyingFishTeam

Web: **www.flyingfishonline.com**

Manor House Activity and Development Centre 18+

Manor House offers a 16-week intensive Outdoor Instructor Training course. During your time on the course you will develop your skills in specific activities: climbing, kayaking, sea kayaking, canoeing, stand up paddleboarding, mountain skills and navigation, cycling, beach lifeguard skills and first aid. You will also work on the theoretical and practical aspects of risk assessments, hazard management, group management and leadership, to name but a few of the modules included.

Twitter: @MActivityCentre

Web: **www.manoractivitycentre.co.uk**

NONSTOP Adventure 17+

NONSTOP Adventure is a family-owned company that runs mountain biking, sailing, skiing and snowboarding training courses. Whether your passion is for the sea or the mountains, there is a course for you. In most cases courses will result in gaining internationally recognised instructor qualifications that could open up exciting employment opportunities worldwide. All courses are run by the industry's top professionals and focus on general improvement as well as gaining professional instructor qualifications. All abilities welcome. ATOL protected.

Twitter: @nonstopsnow

Web: **www.nonstopadventure.com**

Peak Leaders   17+

Peak Leaders' Mountain Bike, Ski and Snowboard courses ensure you will be improving your technical skills, gaining snowsports qualifications, and increasing your understanding of mountain environments, safety and team leading. At the same time, you'll be experiencing life in another culture. There are also nine-week summer break, southern hemisphere courses, with the emphasis on travel and adventure.

Countries: Argentina, Austria, Canada, France, New Zealand, Switzerland

Twitter: @PeakLeaders

Web: **www.peakleaders.com**

ROCK Sailing   16+

ROCK Sailing offer professional Yachtmaster training in the Mediterranean sunshine of Gibraltar, Spain, Portugal and Morocco. They combine professional training with adventure on courses lasting from one to 14 weeks, designed to take a complete newcomer to sailing through to being a fully qualified RYA Yachtmaster and Sailing Instructor.

Countries: Gibraltar

Web: **www.sailinggibraltar.co.uk**

Sporting Opportunities   17+

Sporting Opportunities offer sports coaching volunteer projects which give you the chance to travel to Africa, Asia and South America with likeminded people and volunteer in the community as a sports coach. You will coach sports to children from disadvantaged backgrounds, play sport in the local community and return home with some unforgettable memories. There are a variety of volunteer sports projects to choose from, including football, hockey, rugby, netball and many more. You could find yourself coaching football in India, Argentina or Ghana, or perhaps netball and hockey in South Africa.

Countries: Argentina, Ecuador, Ghana, India, South Africa, St Lucia

Twitter: @SportingOpps

Web: **www.sportingopportunities.com**

United Through Sport   18+

United Through Sport is a UK-registered charity that supports sport and recreation projects in Developing World countries. It particularly focuses on outreach programmes in South Africa, Ghana and Argentina to deliver sporting opportunities for over 15,000 disadvantaged children. The sports programmes are run in local communities, focusing on rugby, netball, cricket, soccer, hockey, swimming and tennis, and offer the opportunity to volunteer as a sports coach.

Countries: Argentina, Ghana, South Africa

Twitter: @utscharity

Web: **www.unitedthroughsport.org**

9. Specific Country-based Organisations

If you know that you want to spend time in one country, you may choose to start here. However, many of the organisations listed under other headings will also have a range of country-specific opportunities on offer.

Alltracks Academy   18+

Alltracks Academy is a family run company that provides ski and snowboard courses in Canada. Alltracks courses include early morning powder runs, racing gates, recognised instructor qualifications, avalanche safety training, and backcountry adventures. Held in the world class ski resort of Whistler, Alltracks courses range from a couple of weeks to the whole season. They make an ideal way for keen skiers or snowboarders to spend a constructive gap year or career break in the mountains, or help kick-start an instructor career.

Countries: Canada

Twitter: @ALLTRACKS

Web: **www.alltracksacademy.com**

Altitude Futures   17+

Altitude Futures offer you the chance to become a fully qualified ski or snowboard instructor. Aimed at competent skiers and snowboarders, the 10-week gap instructor training course provides you with the opportunity to gain a level 1 and 2 BASI (British Association of Snowsport Instructors) ski or snowboard instructor licence, first aid qualification and practical teaching experience whilst skiing or snowboarding at one of the top resorts in the world in Verbier, Switzerland. Each year, Altitude guarantee 10 jobs to the best students.

Countries: Switzerland

Twitter: @AltitudeVerbier

Web: **www.altitude-futures.com**

Americamp   18+

AmeriCamp offers people around the world the chance to work at a summer camp in America, either as a camp counsellor or in a support role behind the scenes. Each year AmeriCamp holds camp fairs in Leeds and London, which give applicants a chance of meeting camp staff face to face and securing a job on the day. It's also a great way of finding the right camp for each person.

Countries: USA

Twitter: @AmeriCamp

Web: **www.americamp.co.uk**

Au Pair in America   18+

Working as an au pair in America can be a good way to discover the USA, as you can experience everyday life with a carefully selected American family and earn weekly pocket money by providing childcare as a nanny or babysitter. Whether you're looking for a year out or just want to work legally abroad, the exchange programmes on the Au Pair in America website give you free time to explore, study, travel and make new friends, together with professional support throughout your stay.

Countries: USA

Twitter: @aupairinamerica

Web: **www.aupairinamerica.com**

Australia Working Holiday   18-30

If you're aged between 18 and 30 and hold a passport for a country or region participating in Australia's Working Holiday Maker programme, you may be eligible to apply for a 12-month visa which enables you to work in Australia. The Australian Government's Working Holiday Maker Programme is a cultural exchange programme which enables young travellers to have an extended holiday and earn money through short-term employment. If you work in Australia's regional areas, in certain circumstances you may even be able to extend your stay for an additional 12 months.

Countries: Australia

Twitter: @australia

Web: **www.immi.gov.au/visitors/working-holiday**

Azafady   18+

Azafady is a sustainable development and conservation organisation that works for a better future for people, communities, and the environment in which they live in south east Madagascar. The approach is one of partnership with local communities to alleviate poverty and support environmental conservation. Integrated sustainable development initiatives support some of the world's most vulnerable people in threatened, irreplaceable environments.

Countries: Madagascar

Twitter: @azafady

Web: **www.madagascar.co.uk**

Bridging The Gap China   18+

Bridging The Gap China offers courses based in the Yunnan province of China that combine Mandarin learning with sightseeing and cultural activities. The courses provide a unique Mandarin learning experience with emphasis on learning whilst travelling. Consequently, they limit the amount of classroom time and ensure a teacher travels with students everywhere. Not only will you get the chance to practise what you've learned in real life situations, but you will also visit some of China's most spectacular sights.

Countries: China

Twitter: @BTG_China

Web: **www.bridgingthegapchina.co.uk**

Camp America   18+

Each year over 7,500 young people take the opportunity to join Camp America and spend the summer in the USA, living and working either with children or behind the scenes as support staff on an American Summer Camp. Following the end of your placement, you'll have up to two months to travel (in total your visa allows for up to four months placement followed by one month of travel but most placements end well within four months).

Countries: USA

Twitter: @CampAmerica69

Web: **www.campamerica.co.uk**

Gap Year South Africa   18+

Gap Year South Africa works extremely closely with under-resourced local South African communities. South African Gap Year projects contribute to social and economic development and address priority areas such as education, health, and social cohesion. Gap Year South Africa offers 3-week, 5-week, 3-month and 5-month project options in Cape Town, and volunteer projects include Teaching and Education, Sports Coaching, Performing Arts, HIV/AIDS Awareness, Care Work, Medical and Veterinary projects and Environmental Awareness, Scuba Diving, Marine Conservation and Surfing Projects.

Countries: South Africa

Twitter: @GapYear_SA

Web: **http://gapyearsouthafrica.com**

Get in2 China   17+

Experience the new Land of Opportunity. Established in 2003, Get in2 China offer the chance to learn Chinese in Beijing or Shanghai. Specialised classes are also available which cover Business Chinese, Chinese Law, News and Current Affairs, and there are courses for both beginners and advanced learners. Paid Internships are also available. In addition, they organise trips for sightseeing and other cultural activities to give you the best Chinese experience possible.

Countries: China

Twitter: @Getin2China

Web: **www.gi2c.org**

Hutong School   16+

Hutong School is a Chinese Language School with locations in Beijing, Shanghai, Brussels & Paris. It specialises in Chinese Language Training and Internship Programmes in China, both in Beijing and Shanghai. The Chinese classes are characterised by their small group size, individual attention to students' needs and highly qualified and motivated teachers. For the Internship Programme the school cooperates with hundreds of partner companies in Beijing and Shanghai who are looking for talented students and young professionals to join their teams for short- or long-term internships in China.

Countries: China

Web: **www.hutong-school.com**

International Academy   18+

International Academy offers ski and snowboard instructor courses in Whistler, Canada. Choose from 4-, 7- or 11-week courses at Whistler's premier ski school and achieve recognised instructor qualifications to teach skiing/snowboarding all over the world.

Countries: Canada

Twitter: @int_academy

Web: **www.international-academy.com**

Karstaway   18+

Karstaway offers a structured, 12-week, three-part programme in China, starting with intensive Mandarin lessons in the village of Yangshou; part two involves setting up and taking part in a community-based sustainable development project, while part three gives you the chance to meet all your fellow volunteers back in Yangshou to reflect on your projects and acknowledge your achievements.

Countries: China

Web: **www.karstaway.com**

Kibbutz Volunteers   18-35

Living and working in a kibbutz community in Israel, carrying out the true principles of a socialistic society, having all work, property and profit equally shared by its members, can form the basis of an intriguing working holiday experience. A holiday with the possibility to meet, live and work with both Israeli youngsters and other kibbutz volunteers from countries and cultures far and near.

Countries: Israel

Twitter: @KIBBUTZwebsi

Web: **www.kibbutz.org.il/eng**

Spark Spanish   17+

SparkSpanish runs dynamic Spanish language courses in the city of El Puerto de Santa María in Andalusia in southern Spain. Experience the local culture and authentic lifestyle that comes with studying in this historic town. Spark also runs Work Experience opportunities where, for a minimum of four weeks, students can use their linguistic, creative and technical abilities to promote and improve all that the school has to offer, all with free accommodation included. SparkSpanish also provides a Demi-pair programme, which gives students the opportunity to stay with a Spanish family whilst gaining experience of looking after children. These opportunities allow students to experience the Spanish way of life whilst simultaneously improving their language skills.

Countries: Spain

Twitter: @SparkSpanish

Web: **www.brightsparkspanish.com**

Visit Oz   17-30

If you are considering a gap year in Australia before you go to university, after you have graduated or at any time before your 31st birthday, Visit Oz guarantees to find you a job on the land or in rural hospitality, as well as providing agricultural or hospitality training. You must have a Working Holiday Visa (or other Visa allowing work) and be prepared to get your hands dirty. Outback farm or station work can include working with horses, cattle and sheep, tractor and header driving, bulldozer work, fencing, mechanical work, and chainsaw work; horse work may be at stables, in trail riding centres, on Host Farms, with racehorses, polo ponies, camp draft horses, or on cattle properties doing bore running, yard work, and maintenance; agricultural bike work is with cattle and sheep. There are so many jobs that it is possible to find something to suit the skills of everybody.

Countries: Australia

Web: **www.visitoz.org**

Volunteering India   18+

Volunteering India provides safe, affordable and meaningful volunteer programmes in India. It offers a variety of volunteer work, cultural exchange, internships, and gap years, where volunteers can choose to work in New Delhi, Palampur/Dharamsala and South India. You could work with orphans, in female empowerment, Health/HIV, teaching English, summer volunteer work or a street children volunteer programme.

Countries: India

Twitter: @indiavolunteer

Web: **www.volunteeringindia.com**

Winant Clayton Volunteers   18+

Winant Clayton has over 50 years' experience placing volunteers in community projects in the United States. You could work with children, the elderly, the homeless, adults with mental health problems and many more. Previous experience is valuable but not essential. You will get direct experience of being part of a local community project in the United States. The work will be challenging and you will discover skills, potential and strengths that you never knew you had.

Countries: USA

Twitter: @WinantClayton

Web: **www.winantclayton.org.uk**

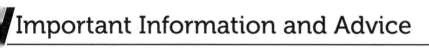# Important Information and Advice

Fundraising

We mention at several points in this publication that it will cost you a fairly considerable sum - often several thousand pounds - to participate in some of the projects listed. This is particularly true of many of the international community, environmental or scientific projects.

For example, to go overseas with Project Trust in 2014, you will be expected to raise £5,600. Project Trust will raise another £600 approximately on your behalf to subsidise the full costs of your year abroad.

Organisations such as Project Trust receive no government assistance and all funds must be raised either by project managers or by volunteers like you.

Given that the aim of this book is to provide you with ideas to help develop your personal, learning and thinking skills, we believe that raising sponsorship can be an important part of this process. It shows others your determination and initiative, and it will help you establish in your own mind just how well you can respond to a challenge. You will have to start by learning how to fundraise and how to make the most of the support available.

Experienced organisers of such projects say that most volunteers are surprised by the response to their efforts and many not only hit their target but actually raise more than the sum required. Only a small number each year have problems and even they can usually be helped to find suitable sponsors.

Should you decide to opt for a project with a sizeable participation fee, you will find that the organisers will normally send you, once accepted, a comprehensive pack containing fundraising ideas and information. In addition, there should be an experienced member of staff able to give you help and advice by email or over the telephone.

The list below should give you a clear idea of the level of fundraising support you should look for when researching a possible project:

- **Advice on fundraising:** Does the selection process introduce the idea of fundraising through a seminar or workshop, encouraging you to think about it constructively?

- **Ongoing support:** What mechanism exists for you to keep the organisers informed of your progress? If you are struggling, do they provide practical advice?

- **Fundraising meetings:** Will you be invited to one or more fundraising meetings, where you can get together with fellow volunteers to share ideas and experiences?

- **Bulletin board:** Is there a website bulletin board allowing you and your fellow volunteers to keep in touch?

Fundraising ideas

The best starting point is always to look inside yourself! There should be no need to turn your life around completely to raise the required funds. Consider what you are already good at and love doing, then think about how you can use your skills to make the money you will need.

If you are good at music, for example, you could try your hand at busking, performing at various events or offering home tuition.

If your interests are more sporting, you could arrange a tournament where teams pay to enter and you provide the service of organising it and setting up suitable prizes.

If you can cook, you could offer a catering service for dinner parties and other social gatherings.

If you are green-fingered, you could offer a gardening service or bring on seeds and cuttings to sell at every opportunity.

If none of these applies, you could simply get a part-time job of any sort and start saving regularly to establish your fund.

Once you have a service to offer, goods to sell or a job to find, turn first to your immediate circle of family, friends and school, college or other social contacts, perhaps in a youth or sports club. If they can't offer you direct support, ask them to think about who they could put you in touch with, or who they might be prepared to approach on your behalf. Before long, you should have a long list of potential customers/employers/sponsors!

While you are raising money, don't forget that you will have other things to buy. You might, for example, need a top quality sleeping bag or rucksack, both of which are likely to be expensive. Baggage insurance is another important extra.

When you go, you will need to take some spending money with you: perhaps around £1,000 for a year-long project, although this can depend upon which country you go to. Even if you can afford it, you shouldn't think of taking so much money overseas that you might be tempted to live and travel in a way that would not sit easily with your role as a volunteer.

Managing Risk

Many of the suggestions in this book contain an element of risk. That is part of their attraction...and you will no doubt see little point in trekking through a jungle or across a mountain range if you are going to be as cosy and safe all the time as you are in an armchair at home. Nevertheless, we could not possibly encourage you to take unnecessary risks and we recommend that you venture overseas only with a reputable organisation with experienced leaders and stringent operating procedures designed to avoid foolhardy misadventure.

We cover a broad range of health and safety issues in our brief quiz on page 107 and we would ask you to spend some time reading this section and visiting the recommended websites. Amongst them, the **Know before you go** site managed by the Foreign and Commonwealth Office is absolutely essential (see page 112).

In addition, we suggest that you use the checklist below when choosing an organisation with which to undertake your trip. This will help to ensure that you are in safe hands and will be travelling responsibly.

- **Crisis Management**: Is there a comprehensive crisis management policy in place? How robust is it and how are staff trained to implement it?

- **UK Support**: Does the organisation maintain a 24-hour emergency telephone line for family and friends in the UK?

- **Insurance**: Does the organisation have a comprehensive company insurance policy with a specialist provider?

- **Leaders**: What is the organisation's recruitment policy in relation to the experience and qualifications of expedition leaders? What knowledge do they have of the countries they work in? Do they have relevant language and first aid skills? Does the Criminal Records Bureau carry out checks of their backgrounds?

- **Risk Assessment**: Do expedition leaders undertake daily monitoring of activities in order to maintain the safety of participants? Are written risk assessments available for consultation? Are participants encouraged to carry out their own risk assessments during an expedition?

- **In-Country Support**: Do leaders have up-to-date contact lists for medical and logistical support in the country you will be visiting?

- **Participant Preparation**: What level of pre-departure training and/or in-country orientation is provided for participants?

- **Equipment**: How often is equipment reviewed and replaced? Is safety equipment provided as standard? Do leaders carry comprehensive first aid kits?

- **Transport**: How do leaders assess in-country transport? Is there a policy regarding the use of public or private transport options? Is road transport undertaken at night?

- **Responsible Travel**: What is the organisation's policy in relation to monitoring and minimising the long-term impact of expeditions such as the one you are considering? Is there a long-term commitment to cultural sensitivity and sustainable development?

- **Financial Transparency**: Can the organisation demonstrate that your financial contributions are spent directly on the project and nowhere else?

- **Feedback**: Is there evidence that feedback from participants and staff is assessed and acted upon where necessary to improve future provision?

A final word. While we have tried our best, as publishers of this book, to ensure that you understand the nature of potential hazards overseas – how to recognise and overcome them – we must stress that you cannot rely totally on us or even on the very best provider of specialist gap year activities. You must use your own common sense and initiative to help you to spend your time as safely as possible.

Finding a Focus

When you have researched the ideas in this book, photocopy these pages and complete a worksheet for each project that interests you. Our 10-point plan will help you focus on finding the right programme to develop your personal learning and thinking skills.

Name of organisation
Type of activity
1. What is it that appeals to me? (Gaining relevant experience, travel, helping others, earning money)
2. Am I eligible? (Right age, available at the right time, suitable qualifications)
3. What exactly will I be doing? (Working with others, undertaking/learning about research methods, cookery)
4. How will I benefit from this programme?
5. How will other people benefit from my involvement?

6. How much will it cost? *(Total budget, raising funds, putting down a deposit)*

7. Who will I be signing up with? *(Commercial company, registered charity)*

8. What do I need to arrange? *(Travel, insurance, health check, vaccinations)*

9. Is there any pre-programme training or briefing?

10. What happens afterwards? *(Debriefing, maintain contact with organisations/ providers, inform future participants, obtain certificate recording my achievements)*

Am I Ready for a Trip Abroad?

If you are planning to travel abroad as part of your personal development, try our brief quiz to see how well prepared you are!

1. **INSURANCE ISSUES**

   (a) I will investigate a range of different types of insurance to cover my travel and placement/project ☐

   (b) I will take out travel insurance for the journeys to and from my placement/project ☐

   (c) I guess that I'm on our family annual travel insurance and that my parents' insurance policies will cover all eventualities ☐

2. **THE COUNTRY I INTEND TO VISIT**

   (a) I have researched the laws and customs of my planned destination as well as the usual food, currency and weather type research ☐

   (b) I have looked at holiday websites to find out about the country I intend to visit ☐

   (c) I'll pick up everything I need to know just by being in the country for several months ☐

3. **VISAS AND PERMITS**

   (a) I have checked out the necessary visas and work permits for the country I intend to visit ☐

   (b) I will see if I need a visa ☐

   (c) Someone will sort out whatever has to happen about a visa for me ☐

4. **HEALTH**

   (a) I will check with my local surgery to see if I need any special injections or healthcare for the country I am visiting a couple of months before the departure date ☐

   (b) I will ask my mum to take a look on the internet to see if there is anything I need to do about health care arrangements for my visit ☐

   (c) I won't bother to do anything special about healthcare as I am young and healthy ☐

5. **SAFETY**

   (a) I have seriously considered a number of ways of ensuring my safety when I am on my placement and I have discussed safety plans with my family ☐

   (b) I am always careful about my well being and I won't need to do anything extra for my placement ☐

   (c) I have no safety worries and I can look after myself ☐

How did you do?

If you answered (a) to all the questions then you have made a good start. All (b) then you have a bit more work to do. All (c) then you really must do a lot more research.

Points to consider

1. Insurance issues

It'll never happen to me!

It can happen to you; things can go wrong. You could fall ill or have an accident; you could have money or luggage stolen; your visit might be cancelled or cut short through injury or illness; your family may need to fly out to be with you if there is a serious incident. So take out insurance. Make sure it's comprehensive and covers you for medical and repatriation costs as well as any dangerous sports or activities.

If you get injured or ill as a result of drugs or alcohol, your insurance may be invalidated and your travel operator can refuse to fly you home.

2. The country I intend to visit

You must read up on the laws and customs of your chosen destination, to avoid offending people or breaking local laws, however unwittingly. The best starting point for this is the Foreign and Commonwealth Office, with its 'Know before you go' awareness campaign aimed at encouraging British travellers to prepare better before going overseas.

Visit the website at: **www.gov.uk/knowbeforeyougo**, and follow them on twitter **@FCOtravel**.

If you are contemplating taking drugs whilst on holiday abroad or bringing some back with you, stop and think - otherwise your trip of a lifetime could end up lasting a lifetime in jail! Bear in mind that: 2,528 British nationals were detained overseas during 2005, a third of them for drugs-related offences; many countries outside the UK refuse to grant bail before trial and may detain people in solitary confinement; you will still get a criminal record in the UK if arrested with drugs abroad; if you've been caught with drugs abroad, you're unlikely ever to be allowed to visit that country again.

3. Passports, Visas and Work Permits

If you wish to travel abroad you must hold a full ten-year passport, even for a day trip. Apply in good time. In the UK, you can get advice from the HM Passport Office website at **www.gov.uk/hm-passport-office** or call them on the Passport Advice Line on 0300 222 0000 (open 7am to 10pm Mon-Fri and 8am to 6pm weekends & public holidays). Some countries have an immigration requirement for a passport to remain valid for a minimum period (usually at least six months) beyond the date of entry to the country. Therefore, if appropriate, ensure your passport is in good condition and valid for at least six months at the date of your return. This is a requirement of the country concerned, not the UK Passport Service, and any questions should be addressed to their Consulate or Embassy.

Outside the UK, you should get advice in an emergency from the nearest British Embassy, High Commission or Consulate. Staff can issue standard replacement passports in most places, and all missions are able to issue emergency passports if more appropriate.

If you plan to travel outside British territories, you may require a visa to enter the country you are going to. Check visa requirements with your project organiser or travel agent or contact the Consulate or Embassy of the country you plan to visit.

If you plan to work outside the European Union, you will need to obtain a valid work permit before you go.

Some Passport Tips:

- Make a note of your passport number, date and place of issue (or take a photocopy), and keep separately in a safe place.
- Check your passport expiry date.
- Write the full details of your next of kin in your passport.
- Leave a photocopy with a friend or relative at home.
- Take a second means of photo-identification with you.
- Keep your passport in the hotel safe and carry a photocopy with you.
- If your passport is lost or stolen overseas, contact the nearest British Embassy, High Commission or Consulate immediately for advice.

4. Health

- Check the Department of Health website at: **www.nhs.uk/Healthcareabroad** for general medical advice for travellers.

- Check what vaccinations you need with your GP at least six weeks before you travel.

- Check if your medication is legal in the country that you are visiting.

- Pack all medication in your hand luggage.

- If you are taking prescribed medication, take the prescription and a doctor's letter with you.

- If you are travelling within the European Economic Area or Switzerland, you should get a free European Health Insurance Card (EHIC) by visiting the Department of Health website as above. You can also obtain the EHIC by completing the Department of Health leaflet 'Health Advice for Travellers' (HAFT), available through most UK Post Offices or by telephoning 0845 606 2030. The EHIC entitles you to free or reduced-cost medical care but you will still need medical and travel insurance.

- Be safe in the sun. Avoid excessive sunbathing, especially between 11am and 3pm, and wear a high factor sunscreen.

- Drink plenty of water. If you drink alcohol or use some kinds of drugs your body can become dehydrated, especially in a hot climate.

- Find out the local emergency number and the address of the nearest hospital when you arrive overseas. Your rep, local guide or project manager should know.

5. Safety

Be aware of what is going on around you and keep away from situations that make you feel uncomfortable. Avoid potentially dangerous 'no-go' areas, in particular after dark. Use your common sense and make sure you are constantly assessing and reassessing your personal safety. Be aware of drugs – these have been used in incidents of rape, so keep your wits about you.

Keep an eye on your possessions. Never leave your luggage unattended or with someone you don't completely trust. Be aware of pickpockets, who tend to operate in crowded areas, and lock up your luggage with padlocks. Make sure you have copies of all important documents such as your passport, tickets, insurance policy, itinerary and contact details. Keep these separate from the originals and leave copies with your family and friends.

Work out how much money you'll need on a daily basis and work to a realistic budget. Be sure to take enough money, as the Foreign and Commonwealth Office can't send you home free of charge if you run out!

Finally, tell friends and family your plans before you go and keep in regular contact, especially if you change your plans. Consider taking a roam-enabled mobile and use text or email to keep in contact. Don't promise too much – promising to call home every day is unrealistic and will only cause your family and friends to worry when you don't!

Further Information

Best Gap Year

This site will provide you with worldwide gap year jobs, courses and travel opportunities, from winter jobs in a ski resort or summer sports teaching courses in Australia to medical projects in China. It offers a huge range of ideas across the world with opportunities to take part in conservation and community projects, teaching, and sports and volunteering. It also provides valuable advice on gap year planning, health and other issues.

Web: **www.bestgapyear.co.uk**

Foreign & Commonwealth Office Website

The Foreign and Commonwealth Office website offers lots of advice for anyone thinking of embarking on gap year travel. From top tips on insurance and money to advice on staying healthy and getting the right visa, you will find all you need to know to plan the safest and most enjoyable gap year travel.

Phone: 0845 850 2829

Twitter: @fcotravel

Web: **www.gov.uk/gap-year-foreign-travel-advice**

www.gov.uk/knowbeforeyougo

Gap Advice

Gapadvice.org was founded in June 2005 to provide an independent source of impartial advice and information for people of all ages looking to take a gap week, month or year. It provides advice for young people after leaving school, for undergraduates and those who have just graduated as well as those looking for career breaks. It contains information on considering your gap year, investigating it, organising it, doing it etc., all covered in a comprehensive plan.

Web: **www.gapadvice.org**

Gapyear.com

Gapyear.com is a social media and travel advice website created by backpackers, for backpackers, devoted to giving you everything you could possibly need when planning or taking a gap year. It hosts and supports a community that is passionate about real travel and ready to share experience and advice. The community is backed up with expert guides.

Twitter: @gapyeardotcom

Web: **www.gapyear.com**

Hostelling International

Youth hostels can provide you with reliable, reasonably priced accommodation in many parts of the world. Hostelling International is the brand name of more than 90 Youth Hostel Associations in 90 countries, operating 4,000 plus hostels. Unlike bland motels, impersonal hotels or dodgy backpacker rooms, youth hostels are usually fun, lively meeting places, full of like-minded people.

Twitter: @Hostelling

Web: **www.hihostels.com**

InterHealth Worldwide

InterHealth Worldwide is an international medical charity that specialises in providing detailed and specific travel health advice tailored to remote and exotic destinations. With services such as a personal MyHealth portal on its website, it is easily accessible remotely. The online shop can supply everything from first aid kits to mosquito nets and water purification tablets.

Twitter: @InterHealth

Web: **www.interhealthworldwide.org**

Objective Travel Safety

During Objective's Gap Safety courses, students are given advice, warnings and responses to various situations they may face while travelling. The course is designed to teach the individual how to evaluate situations so they can avoid trouble and to give them the confidence to get off the beaten track and explore.

Twitter: @ObjectiveTravel

Web: **www.objectivegapyear.com**

STA Travel

STA Travel are specialists in cheap flights, adventure trips, insurance, bus tickets, rail passes, car/campervan hire, hostels, and travel deals for young people. They also have several pages of gap year travel tips on their website.

Twitter: @STATravel_UK

Web: **www.statravel.co.uk**

World Travel Guide

Want a heads up on what the visa regulations are for visitors to India, how much duty free you can bring back from France, what the main sights are in Yemen or when the best time of year to go to Jamaica is? It's all available here, and quickly searchable by country or region.

Twitter: @WTGTravelGuide

Web: **www.worldtravelguide.net**

Suggested Reading List

Gap Years - The Essential Guide
- Emma Jayne Jones, Need2Know, 2013

Backpacking: The ultimate guide to first time around the world travel
- Michael Huxley, CreateSpace Independent Publishing Platform, 2013

The Gap-year Guidebook 2014: Everything You Need to Know About Taking a Gap-year or Year Out
- Jonathan Barnes, John Catt Educational Ltd, 2012

Your Gap Year: The Most Comprehensive Guide to an Exciting and Fulfilling Gap Year
- Susan Griffith, Crimson Publishing, 2012

The Rough Guide to First-Time Around The World
- Doug Lansky, Rough Guides, 2013

Work Your Way Around the World
- Susan Griffith, Vacation Work, 2011

Lonely Planet's Best Ever Travel Tips
- Tom Hall, Lonely Planet Publications, 2010

The Backpacker's Bible
- Suzanne King, Anova, 2012

Volunteer: A Traveller's Guide to Making a Difference Around the World
- Lonely Planet Publications, 2013

Green Volunteers 8th Edition: The World Guide to Voluntary Work in Nature Conservation
- Fabio Ausenda, Green Volunteers, 2011

Archaeo-Volunteers: The World Guide to Archaeological and Heritage Volunteering
- Fabio Ausenda, Vacation Work, 2009

Improve Your Grades - Revision Courses

Improve Your Grades - Revision Courses

The following independent colleges offer specific retake and intensive revision courses, giving you the opportunity to improve your performance in a wide range of subjects during the Easter vacation.

Abbey Colleges

The Abbey Colleges are part of the Alpha Plus Group – formerly Davies, Laing and Dick Education Group – which currently comprises twenty independent schools, colleges and sixth form colleges. Abbey Colleges in Birmingham, Cambridge, London and Manchester offer intensive retake courses for GCSE and AS and A Level.

Web: **www.abbeycolleges.co.uk**

Ashbourne Independent Sixth Form College, London

Easter revision courses seek to motivate students to strive for the highest grades at A level and GCSE, and to develop independence and self-reliance. As a private college, Ashbourne is able to offer classes which average five students per group.

Twitter: @AshbourneLondon

Web: **www.ashbournecollege.co.uk**

Collingham College, Kensington, London

Intensive tuition in small classes enables individual needs to be met. Groups are Board-specific as appropriate and are formed according to syllabus, topics, texts and so on. The courses are planned to give a clear understanding of the essentials of the syllabus and to teach exam techniques, so that you can use your knowledge to best effect.

Web: **www.collingham.co.uk**

Duff Miller Sixth Form College, South Kensington, London

Duff Miller offers Easter Revision courses across a wide range of A Level and GCSE subjects. They act to inspire, motivate and fulfil academic potential. The primary emphasis of the revision courses is to enhance subject knowledge and establish a rigorous, disciplined and effective approach, resulting in peak exam performance.

Web: **www.duffmiller.com**

Harrogate Tutorial College

Easter Revision courses at Harrogate are designed to help students achieve examination grades well above those they originally expected, but are not intended for students who have done little or no work in their subjects. The small classes – average four, maximum eight students – generate an informal, student-centred approach with the emphasis on high quality work.

Web: **www.htcuk.org**

Justin Craig Education

Established in 1981 and with more than 20 centres around the country, Justin Craig Education provides GCSE, AS and A2 group revision courses. Offering small, informal tutorial groups taught by friendly, enthusiastic and experienced tutors, Justin Craig Education has helped over 100,000 students achieve the grades needed to get into their chosen universities.

Twitter: @JustinCraig_

Web: **www.justincraig.ac.uk**

Lansdowne College, London

Lansdowne College has run Easter Revision courses for over 20 years, helping students to realise their full academic potential at both GCSE and A Level, and enabling them to progress onto their chosen path for their studies. Students are often unaware of exactly what examiners are looking for and subsequently unsure of what makes an A grade answer. The Easter Revision courses remedy this by focusing not just on the subject content, but also on extensive and comprehensive examination preparation, including a mock examination at the end of the course.

Web: **www.lansdownecollege.com**

Mander Portman Woodward (MPW)

MPW is an independent sixth-form college group, with colleges in London, Birmingham and Cambridge. In addition to full-time GCSE courses, AS courses and A2 courses over a very wide range of subjects and with no restrictions on subject combinations, MPW offers intensive A level and GCSE retake courses and revision courses over Easter. Characterising all courses is an absolute maximum of eight students within any one class and a strong emphasis on exam technique and exam practice.

Web: **www.mpw.co.uk**

Millfield School, Somerset

On its Easter Revision course, Millfield offers specialist tuition at GCSE, AS and A2 level, in a broad range of subjects to small groups of students, providing a balance of taught content and rehearsal of technique. Students from all schools are welcome. Courses are offered on both a residential and non-residential basis.

Web: **www.millfieldenterprises.com**

Oxford Tutorial College

Oxford Tutorial College organises short intensive revision courses at Easter, both at A level and GCSE, as well as supplementary teaching at other times throughout the year to support the work being done at school. There is a mixture of individual tuition and small group seminars.

Web: **www.otc.ac.uk**

Rochester Independent College, Kent

Intensive Easter revision courses at Rochester provide an opportunity to gain an overview of the syllabus and a chance to practise applying knowledge to real examination questions. This helps with recall of facts and hones skills required for accurate question interpretation and structuring full and concise answers. Most importantly, the courses give a real confidence boost at a crucial time.

Twitter: @RICollege

Web: **www.rochester-college.org**

Taster Courses

Taster Courses

Almost all universities and colleges organise pre-application Open Days, giving you an opportunity to visit the campus, meet some of the staff and students, and attend a short talk on a subject in which you are interested. Details of these days can be found in the **Open Days** information on the UCAS website at: www.ucas.com.

We focus here on courses that some universities and colleges provide to give you a more detailed opportunity to experience academic and social life on campus. Please note that we refer to **Taster Courses** for the sake of clarity but universities are independent institutions and don't always use the same terminology. It is, therefore, not unusual to find **Taster Courses** described as Summer Schools or Academies (at any time of year!), Campus Days or Find Out More Days.

Duration

Course lengths vary: some are one-day courses only, others may last a weekend or even a week. Most courses are free (although you will normally have to pay for travel and accommodation). You may have the chance to stay overnight on campus.

Format

Most **Taster Courses** include lectures, discussions and tutorial sessions, so that you can meet the departmental staff and get hands-on experience using the facilities. This can provide an important insight into how the university or college operates. **Taster Courses** should also allow you to find out about other aspects of undergraduate life, such as sporting, musical, drama and cultural activities, accommodation and other amenities.

Benefits of Attending a Taster Course

- You are more likely to choose a higher education course to suit your interests and abilities and to avoid an unsuitable one.

- You can highlight your attendance in the personal statement section of your UCAS application.

- You may find that a course or campus is not for you, and decide to reject it in favour of others.

- You can discuss your impressions with admissions tutors at universities or colleges during interviews.

Science and Technology tasters

In addition to the Taster Courses listed on the following pages, see Section 3 for details of the science and technology tasters, particularly those organised by Headstart and the Smallpeice Trust.

University of Aberdeen Summer School for Access

The Summer School is a ten-week, full-time programme of study, which runs from June to August each year. You have to undertake four courses and complete coursework and exams, on successful completion of which (at minimum Grade 12 out of 20) you will be guaranteed a place on an undergraduate programme at the University of Aberdeen. You may also use the Summer School for entry into other universities across the UK, although you must contact the other institutions and agree their entry requirements before you start.

If you are a student from within the European Union, you are not normally required to pay tuition fees for the Summer School and free accommodation may also be available, based on household income and expenditure.

For further details email: **SSA-Aberdeen@abdn.ac.uk** or visit the website: **www.abdn.ac.uk/lifelonglearning/ssa**

Aberystwyth University

The Schools and Colleges Liaison Team can arrange on-campus taster days and workshops for school and college groups with an opportunity to stay overnight in a hall of residence. Please email **marketing@aber.ac.uk** if you would like to discuss the day/residential programmes available at the University.

Aston University, Birmingham

Aston organises a range of Masterclasses and Sixth Form Conferences providing a taster of university life in specific subject areas including Biology, Business, Chemistry, English Language, Engineering, Law, Mathematics, Modern Foreign Languages (French, German and Spanish), Optometry, Pharmacy, Psychology, Politics and Sociology.

For further information please contact Angela Morris at **morrisa@aston.ac.uk**; telephone: 0121 204 4787; website: **www.aston.ac.uk/schliaison**

University of Birmingham School of Engineering

There may be some opportunities to experience engineering by attending one-day taster courses in the five Schools of Engineering during the spring/summer. For full details visit the website at **www.birmingham.ac.uk**.

University College, Birmingham

University College offers a Summer School in various subjects. Full time – 3 days/2 nights. Limited spaces only. Also Master Classes offered in a choice of 9 subjects on one morning or afternoon. Limited spaces only.

For further details on their summer school and master classes, please contact Ruth Walton, telephone: 0121 232 4042, email: **ruthwalton@ucb.ac.uk**, or visit the website: **www.ucb.ac.uk**

Bradford College

The college offers a variety of taster days for courses in both further and higher education. To attend or request more information about taster days, contact the Education Liaison Team Leader, telephone 01274 433084 or email: **educationliaison@bradfordcollege.ac.uk**

University of Chichester

Several departments at the University of Chichester run taster days, in which you can sample lectures or participate in workshops. In some cases, these events are open to all prospective applicants, while others invite people who have already applied, to help them make their final choice. You can book online for taster days – usually held in March/April – in the following areas: Business and IT Management, Humanities, Arts, Sport Science and Sports Studies, Education and Teaching, and Social Sciences.

Further information can be found at: **www.chi.ac.uk/tasterdays**

Cornwall College, Newquay

Offers university course taster days on various dates between October and June. These taster days give prospective students the opportunity to look around the campus and its facilities, talk to programme lecturers and discover more about the course of interest. Students can also find out about tuition fees and the financial support available, meet current students and discover more about student life in Cornwall. Booking is essential. For further details, please telephone 01637 857 957 or visit the website at: **www.cornwall.ac.uk**

University of Exeter, Penryn Campus Open Days

As a visitor to our small and friendly Penryn campus, near Falmouth, you can spend a day attending sample lectures, discussing programme options with our leading academics and finding out from current students what it's really like to study at a top research-led university in a beautiful location. There are also tours of the campus and facilities. Prospective Geology and Mining Engineering students can visit our test mine. At the Penryn Campus programmes include Biosciences, English, Environmental Science, Flexible Combined Honours, Geography, Geology, History, Mathematics and the Environment, Mining Engineering, and Politics and Renewable Energy.

For full details, visit the website at: **www.exeter.ac.uk/visit**

University of Exeter, College of Engineering, Mathematics and Physical Sciences

The Pre-University Physics Course is offered in June/July. For further details please contact **pupc@exeter.ac.uk** or visit the website at: **www.exeter.ac.uk/pupc**

Glyndwr University

Glyndwr University hosts a number of open days and interactive sessions each year which could help you if you have not yet made the decision to enter HE. The focus is on demystifying HE, increasing awareness of the opportunities available, answering questions about finance and support, building confidence and skills, and getting to know the campus and facilities.

For further details visit the website at: **www.glyndwr.ac.uk**

University of Leeds

Leeds has an international reputation for its teaching and research. We offer a range of courses and opportunities to help you develop into an articulate, highly-skilled and confident graduate ready to pursue the career of your choice. Find out more about Leeds and what they offer at the website, **www.leeds.ac.uk**, and visit one of their open days. If you make Leeds one of your five choices you may be invited for a detailed departmental visit.

Register for open days at: **www.leeds.ac.uk/opendays** or email **opendays@leeds.ac.uk**

London University Taster Course Programme

With over 160 courses in 70 different subject areas at numerous university institutions, the Taster Course Programme provides the opportunity to experience life as a university student in the subject area of your choice, ranging from medicine and dentistry to drama and film studies. The taster courses last from half a day to one week, and are usually available between March and July. All courses are non-residential and provided free of charge. You may apply for up to three courses via the online application form. The Careers Group, University of London administers the programme and in 2013 the following colleges participated. (Visit the website at **www.london.ac.uk/tasters** or email: **tastercourses@london.ac.uk** for an up-to-date list of participating colleges):

Birkbeck:
> Arts and Humanities
> Criminology & Criminal Justice
> English Literature
> Film
> History of Art
> Journalism
> Languages and Culture
> > (French, German, Japanese, Portuguese, Spanish)
> Law
> Management and Organizational Psychology
> Media
> Philosophy
> Psychology
> Theatre Studies

BPP University College:
> Accounting
> Banking & Finance
> Business
> Law

City University, London:
> Accounting and Finance
> Aeronautical Engineering
> Automotive & Mechanical Engineering
> Biomedical Engineering
> Business Studies & Management
> Civil Engineering
> Computing
> Economics
> Electrical, Electronic and Computer Engineering
> Film, music, and the arts: Creative industries
> International Politics

City University, London (continued):

Investment and Financial Risk Management;
Banking and Finance
Journalism
Law
Midwifery
Music
Nursing
Optometry
Psychology
Radiography
Sociology
Speech and Language Therapy

Courtauld Institute of Art:

History of Art

Goldsmiths:

Computing
Design
English
History
History of Art
Management
Media & Communications, Journalism
Music Computing
Politics
Psychology
Sociology

Heythrop College:

Abrahamic Faiths
Philosophy
Philosophy, Religion & Ethics
Theology

Imperial College:

Computing
Maths and Computing

King's College:

Biomedical Engineering
Chemistry
Classics
English and Comparative Literature
English Language & Communication
European Studies and European Politics
French
Geography
German
Global Health & Social Medicine

Informatics
Language, Literature & Culture of the Hispanic & Lusophone Worlds
Liberal Arts
Maths
Midwifery
Nursing
Nutrition
Philosophy
Physics
Science Engagement & Communication
Theology and Religious Studies

London Metropolitan:

Art & Design
Business
Criminology and Sociology
Early Years Teaching, Early Childhood Studies and Education Studies
English, Journalism and Media
Health, Social Care, Youth and Community Work
Law
Politics, Governance & International Relations

London School of Economics & Political Science (LSE):

Anthropology
Geography & Environment
International History
Law
Philosophy
Sociology

London South Bank University:

Engineering Product Design
Product Design

Queen Mary, University of London:

Astrophysics
Business and Management Studies
Dentistry
Economics
Electronics and Computing
Environmental Science
Geography
Mathematics
Maths with Business and Finance
Physics
Pure Mathematics

Royal Holloway:

Biosciences
Classical World
Comparative Literature and Culture

Royal Holloway (continued):
Computer Science
English
French
German
Geography
History
Italian
Mathematics
Media Arts
Music
Philosophy
Physics
Politics
Psychology
Spanish

Royal Veterinary College:
Bioveterinary Sciences
Veterinary Medicine
Veterinary Nursing

School of Oriental & African Studies (SOAS):
Arts and Humanities
Languages and Cultures
Law
Social Science

St George's Hospital:
Medicine

The Careers Group:
Careers in Law
Careers in Medicine
Career Options for Science, Technology, Engineering and Maths

UCL:
Anthropology
Arts and Sciences
Classics and Ancient World Studies
Construction
East European Languages
Electronic and Electrical Engineering
Engineering
English
Medical Physics
Science and Religion
Science and Technology Studies
Women in Engineering
Women in Mathematics
Women in Technology

University of East London:
Architecture, Computing and Engineering
Psychology

University of Greenwich:
Computing
Film and TV Production
Games and Digital Media
Mathematics

University of London Institute in Paris:
French

University of West London:
Aviation and Tourism Management

University of Westminster:
Biology

Loughborough University

Engineering Experience - Loughborough's Schools of Engineering have been running this highly successful two-day event for the last 24 years. Open to year 12 students, the event gives an insight into engineering at university. During their stay at the University, students have the opportunity to visit a number of departments including Aeronautical and Automotive Engineering, Mechanical and Manufacturing Engineering, Electronic and Electrical Engineering, Chemical Engineering and Materials), learn about different engineering options, talk to lecturers and tutors about engineering courses and experience student accommodation, the Students' Union and catering. Spaces are limited.

For further information visit the website at: **www.engexp.info** or email: **engexp@lboro.ac.uk**

Newcastle College

Taster courses are offered in Art and Design, Beauty and Complementary Therapies; Business Management and Computing; Construction and Civil Engineering; Engineering and Science; Health Care and Public Services; Music, Media and Performing Arts; Sport and Exercise; Travel, Aviation and Hospitality. Taster courses are usually run during school holidays.

For further details visit the website at: **www.ncl-coll.ac.uk**; telephone: 0191 200 4000 or email: **enquiries@ncl-coll.ac.uk**

Newcastle University

Newcastle University holds a number of Visit Days each year, which are an excellent opportunity to see the University at its bustling best and discover more about the subjects you're interested in. To find out about the Visit Days and other opportunities to get a feel for student life at Newcastle visit the website: **www.ncl.ac.uk/undergraduate/visit**

University of Reading Food and Nutritional Sciences Summer School

Are you a young scientist with an interest in a career in food? The Department of Food and Nutritional Sciences at Reading offers an annual short introductory course in late June/early July for lower 6th form students (Year 12). The course is sponsored by manufacturing and retail companies in the food industry.

For further information, email: **food@reading.ac.uk** or visit the website: **www.reading.ac.uk/food**

Royal Agricultural University

The RAU's Land-Based Careers Taster Course is a two-day residential short course and is aimed at 16 to 19-year-olds (although mature students may also find it of interest). It gives an insight into the career opportunities that exist in the food and land-based industries, both in the UK and worldwide. It also provides an opportunity to learn more about the courses on offer at the College.

For full details and a downloadable application form, visit the website at: **www.rau.ac.uk** or email: **jenny.maguire@rau.ac.uk**

Shrewsbury College of Arts and Technology

Secondary school pupils from around Shropshire are invited to 'taster sessions' at Shrewsbury College to give them an insight into life in Further Education. The College has three campuses, at London Road, Radbrook and Telford. Tasters at London Road will include Accounting, Art & Design, Business, Catering, Computing & IT, Performing Arts, Public Services, Sports Studies and Travel & Tourism. Also at London Road will be tasters run by the Technology Faculty, including Brickwork, Carpentry & Joinery, Painting & Decorating, Electrical Installation, Plumbing, Engineering and Motor Vehicle. At Radbrook campus, pupils can sample Childcare, Hair &

Beauty and Health & Social Care. At their Telford Construction Centre tasters are available in Plastering, Brickwork and Painting & Decorating.

For further details visit the website at: **www.shrewsbury.ac.uk** or telephone 01743 342332.

University of Southampton

The University of Southampton will be hosting open days for prospective students and their parents in July and September. The programme of events includes both general and subject-specific presentations and drop-in points as well as tours of academic schools, campuses and halls of residence. Advance booking is highly recommended.

For further information, please visit:
www.southampton.ac.uk/visit

Sparsholt College Hampshire

If you are considering a career in the land, environment or animal industries, Sparsholt College Hampshire offers a number of taster days. Subjects include Agriculture, Animal Management, Arboriculture and Forestry, Equine, Fishery Studies, Gamekeeping and Conservation, Horticulture, Land-based Engineering, Sport and Public Services. These special programmes can be valuable in helping to make course and career choices.

Full details are available from **www.sparsholt.ac.uk** or can be obtained by emailing: **courses@sparsholt.ac.uk**

Sutton Trust Summer School

Sutton Trust Summer Schools offer an opportunity to try University life for over 1,700 young people every year. The programme consists of lectures, seminars and tutorials but also various social activities. The programme runs at Bristol, Cambridge, Edinburgh, Nottingham, St Andrews, Durham, Imperial College London and UCL.

The Sutton Trust Summer Schools are open to all students in Year 12 at maintained schools or colleges in the UK. Places are limited. Priority will be given to students:

- whose family background has no history of higher education

- whose parents are in non-professional occupations

Sutton Trust Summer School (continued)

- who have achieved at least 5 A/A*s at GCSE

- Please visit the website for full eligibility criteria

Courses are available in areas including: English, History of Art, Theology, Drama, Languages, History, Philosophy, Sciences, Computer Science, Maths, Social Sciences, Economics, Politics, Law, Engineering, Medicine, Dentistry and Veterinary Science.

The Sutton Trust meets all costs incurred by the student including travel, food and accommodation. For full details, visit the website: **www.suttontrust.com**

Swansea University

Taster courses are available in various subject areas and have previously included Psychology, Engineering and Science as detailed below. Visit the website **www.swansea.ac.uk** for full details.

Engineering Summer School is open to any Year 12 student who is considering applying for an Engineering degree. There is a small cost to include all food, accommodation and activities. You can register your interest by emailing **engineering@swansea.ac.uk**

Headstart Cymru Engineering Summer School is for students living or studying in Wales. It is similar to the format above but run in partnership with EESW Stem Cymru and subsidised places are available. For further information and an application form visit the Headstart Cymru website. Applicants must apply directly through EESW Stem Cymru.

Psychology afternoons are usually held in February. Prospective students can meet academic staff and attend an introductory talk and various taster talks. Places must be booked in advance via **psychology.admissions@swansea.ac.uk**. For further details contact Karen Huxtable – telephone 01792 513023.

At the Science Summer School students can experience a series of taster days in Swansea's five College of Science departments carrying out experiments and workshops in bioscience, computing, geography, maths and physics. Contact **ross.davies@swansea.ac.uk**.

Warwickshire College

Warwickshire College open events are offered at their centres in Leamington, Rugby, Moreton Morrell, Warwick and Henley-in-Arden in Warwickshire and Pershore in Worcestershire. The college also offers taster days in land-based subjects such as equine, agriculture, countryside, horticulture, animal welfare and veterinary nursing at Moreton Morrell and Pershore. These taster events provide an opportunity to experience what it's like to be a student at Warwickshire College – they cover practical hands-on sessions and lecture samples in a friendly environment and in a great countryside location.

For further details of general open events and taster days available, visit the website at: **www.warwickshire.ac.uk/events**

University of the West of Scotland

A Summer School is offered at the Dumfries Campus in business and computing. It gives the opportunity to try out new subjects, experience university life, enhance your qualifications, develop study skills, boost confidence and improve your employability. Apply online at: **www.uws.ac.uk/study-at-uws/summer-schools**

Introductory-level study is also available in other subjects at campuses in Ayr, Dumfries, Hamilton and Paisley, e.g. First Steps to Nursing, First Steps to University, First Steps in IT and Career Planning. These modules are delivered on a part-time basis starting in September, January and June each year. For details telephone 0800 027 1000 or visit the website: **www.uws.ac.uk**

University of York

The University of York subject taster days are aimed at students in Year 12, who would like an insight into degree-level study before applying to university. Their taster days allow visitors to hear about multiple related academic disciplines on one day, while subject conferences focus on just one academic discipline.

For students who are not sure about what they want to study, or whether university is the right option, taster days are the perfect opportunity to find out more.

For full details, visit the website: **www.york.ac.uk/tasterdays** or contact the student recruitment team by phone: 01904 323196; email: **admissions-liaison@york.ac.uk**

Subject Index

Index of Taster Course Subjects

Organisation Index

Geographical Index